Childre
Get Out of the
Mentali

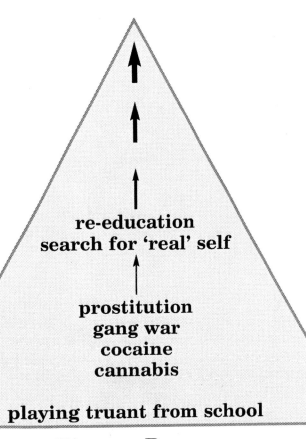

Know Thyself!
Maslow's theory

↑

↑

↑

**re-education
search for 'real' self**

↑

**prostitution
gang war
cocaine
cannabis**

playing truant from school

Pitman Browne

i

Any clarification or authorisation for use of any thing required with respect to
the actual contents of these pages
may be sought by making contact with

Pitman Browne
The Editor
Kitabu-Pet

Publishers of thought-provoking books

such as "Inklings of a Black Christ"/1997 (ISBN 0 95314930 7)
and "Wishing can be Dangerous"/1999 (ISBN 0 95314931 5)

Whilst drawing upon those attributes ascribed to a highly efficient e-mailing service,
you are invited to send your letters to:
pitman_browne@hotmail.com
or phone (0115) 845 0034

Alternatively, please feel free to visit my website on:
http://www.kitabu.pro-designs.com

"Children get out of the Ghetto Mentality"
was published in August 2000
by Kitabu-Pet

ISBN 0 95314932 3

Printed by 4 Sheets Design & Print
197 Mansfield Road, Nottingham NGI 3FS, England

FOREWORD

A special note from the Principal of

The People's College Nottingham

"POWERFUL IMAGES OF FRUSTRATION AND EXPLOITATION!"

It is with pleasure that I recommend to the reader the latest work of Pitman Browne. This is Pitman's third book. His previous works dealt with the theory that Jesus Christ's Black African roots have been overlooked by Western scholars, and Astral Projection through strong fantasies can influence not only our present life, but life after death. This third book deals with the experiences of many young Black people — growing up at the margins of social life, preyed upon by drug pushers and pimps.

This book is demanding and challenging like Pitman himself. Pitman is a self-starter in life. He has struggled to gain education and learning. He believes that knowledge liberates us from our chains, and allows us to stand as free men and women. Pitman has achieved a B.A. Honours degree in Humanities from the Open University which is no mean feat in itself. However, he is largely a self-taught scholar: a true autodidact in the Honourable tradition of the great 19th Century self-taught radicals whose culture was immortalised by Robert Tressel in 'The Ragged Trousered Philanthropists'.

Hardly surprising therefore that Pitman does not take an easy approach to familiar problems, but seeks to find and express the voice of the young themselves. Pitman Browne is known as a Performance Poet, a talented speaker with clear views; one who is always interested in the views of others, at the same time he relishes the cut and thrust of debate and controversy. This book with its combination of declamation, poetic engagement and fictionalised documentary, evokes very powerful images of frustration and exploitation. Pitman aims to engage with young people who have dropped out of school, who have left school with no hope and who are hanging about the streets. He dramatises the self-inflicted wounds of drug abuse and gang violence, in language which is vivid.

Not surprisingly, Pitman urges the young to value education and learning as the means to greater freedom. Pitman's learning focuses on the little acknowledged contribution Black people have made to life. His message is a powerful one; he says:

> "Try and get!
> Try and get! Me say
> Try and get back de
> Self-esteem".

This may not be an easy message for many young people or their parents, but I am sure that he is right: pride and self-esteem cannot co-exist with ignorance and exploitation.

I hope that those who read Pitman Browne are stimulated to take action in their own lives, and work to improve the lives and prospects of their fellow citizens.

Mr John Rudd, MA FRSA
Principal
People's College
Nottingham
2000-03-15

SMOKE DE ASH AN' TEEF LOTS OF PETTY CASH

Roydel 'Youth Man'

Jah Rastafari, blessed love to one and all! I — and — I name is Roydel 'Youth Man' Lothian, and I man is 22. All ova St Ann's me grow up. Me grow up een a dis town — right brethren? I mus tek dis opportunity to draw de attention of de youth man dem to sum a de tings dem dat we as young bwoys/men get up to.

When me did younger me used to teef. (Dem call it 'thief' — me call it 'teef'!). Me teef in a de house and me Mom used to beat me. Den, wen me go out a street me teef from everybody — anybody! Me teef wen me go a school.

I man purposely get m'self een a trouble, so dem put me to stand outside d' headmaster's office. I nevva mind, because once outside dere I could a sneak inside an' teef d'dinna money from off de Secretary's desk. De best day fe teef de children dinna money was Munday. Golly gosh! Laud man: every Munday I man end up wid a whole heep — some nuff nuff money!

Some good teefin', I man bad, bad, bad fe true!! By d'time I wuz 11, I wuz told to go on de paper round fe go earn me own money. Since d'paper round paid only £12-a-week, it wasn't long before I man start fe teef from behind de counter. Mannn? I would tek £20 bags of coins and hide dem on de roof of de school, so at evenin' time m'pockets dem full... I man end up wid a whole heep — some nuff nuff money!

DEN M' START FE SMOKE DE WEED...

When I was 14, me an m'school friend dem wuz smokin' weed full time. At break time we used to go into de woods fe a good smokin' session. Den afta school, one of m'frends used to tek me to his parents' house. <u>His parents didn't mind us smokin' weed</u>. <u>In fact, dem even give we weed an ash fe smoke</u>. Dat good man! I man luv fe go at dem house fe go get de weed. I-an-I man even start fe teef dem money an so forth. Wen m' smoke ash, it mek me 'ave headache, but wen I man smoke de weed, it mek me feel good good fe true. Wen me a smoke de weed m'eye dem red. De more m'smoke, d'more me teef money fe buy drugs, and d' more me teef money f' buy drugs, d'more me smoke d'weed. Me luv de weed bad bad bad man! Me luv de weed yu se'?

Before long, I man a start fe shop-lift wid m'friend dem, an' hear wah? I-an-I man start fe burgle house so me can get more money fe go buy weed. All day long, we a smoke weed, an' all night long, we a look house fe burgle. Me burgle house fe two years on de stretch. I man bruk de whole a de house dem een a my street wey m'live. Teef video; Teef jewellery; teef money. De people dem nevva like it. Dem go call de Police fe arres' me. 'Bout 5 or 6 times dem arres' me. Mee no fright'n fe no Police. Me only frighten fe me Mom because she w' tell me off! Anyway de Police dem couldn't sen' me go a prizen 'cause I man wuz under age yu se'. As soon as me turn 16, dem lock me up fe 3 months.

NO MORE TEEFIN': A PACK IT IN!

Afta me come out a prizen, me nevva badda fe teef no more. I man decide fe behave m'self. Wen m'did in a de prizen me Mom write me; 8 page! 8 page a nuff nuff page! Fe d'nex 3 years no more teefin'! Finish!! Pack it in!!! I man start Agency werk day job like painting an'decorating an'joinery. In between jobs me wuz unemployed. For a while a nevva bother fe teef no more 'cause me Mom write 8 page full a letta, wen me did een a prizen.

I-AN-I MAN SELL DE CRACK AN' DE COCAIN!

I man get pissed-off: pure odd jobs and no money. Wat is pittance? Pittance is peanuts! I-an-I no want no pittance, I a look some big big money, so a start f'sell de weed. Pure foolishniss a gwaan, so 'Youth Man' Roydel begin to sell de cocaine, sell de crack an' sell de heroin. Bang! Liftoff!! All ova de place!!! Laud man, night an' day, dem a run come fe de ting. My phone a 'blow' (ringing) all mornin' right through tell midnite. Den de money: yes Rasta. De big money dem start to roll...yes man... a so me like it!!!

ME POCKETS DEM RAMMED FULL A'MONEY!

Thousands a' Pounds. I-an-I mek thousands a'Pounds in days! In a de dark dark night between 2:00 an' 3:am wen I-an-I come home an' start count-out me monies on me bed... empty me two top pockets: empty me two side an' back pockets... nottin'. NOTTIN' BUT SUM BIG BIG MONIES. Yet, if I did want to be a geedy man I couldda mek more. But a wuzn't greedy at all. De only people I really did come in contact wid was me family. I-an-I begin to close-off from de whole o'me friends dem. I used to tink sey money could a mek yu happy, but I wuz wrong. De more I accumulate de money, de more a wouldda watch other people dressed-up in a dem dere name brand clothes, an' drivin' dem dere flash cars. None a de spiritual stuff, just pure material tings wuz on me mind.

DEN A STARTED GOIN' OUT WID LISA

She wuz 18. I wuz 20. Meetin' her wuz like a new beginnin', a fresh breath of inspiration comin' from another plane of life. Quietly confident, hailing from a sheltered family, Roman Catholic upbringing an' all dat... Being with har kinda gave me time to analyse m'personality, an' go into parts of m'self (me 'inner' or 'real' self) which I did spend m'life runnin' away from.

FE DE FIRST TIME IN M' LIFE I A START FE PRAY!

Me did borrow a tape from m'Mom called 'Tapping de Power Within' by Iyanla Vanzant. Jus by listenin' to dis tape, it put me in de frame of mind to ask forgiveness from people I had hurt, upset... all de kids whose dinna money I did teef an' all de people whose houses m'did bruk fe go tek dem stereo, an dem video an dem money... I did really did feel bruk-up fe true! Man? I-an-I man really sorry. Me pray. Yes, fe d'first time in a m'whole life me pray to de Creator fe forgiveness an'healin'.

WID LISA M' LIFE START FE CHANGE

Me nevva care 'bout money any more. In fact, I man stop supplying de customers wid crack, cocain and heroin. It wuzn't easy since de phone still keep buzzin' from mornin' till night. All a wanted out a life was to be righteous and be with Lisa. We finally decided to live together. But I man started getting' a lot a'pressure from har dad. Dis man tried every-ting fe split us up. Him wouldda phone de Police an' tell dem I wuz sellin' drugs. Him wouldda phone de Drugs Hot Line 14 times a day, tellin' dem m'name an'wat I wuz up to. I believe if it wusn't for de Creator, I wouldda get lock-up because of 'im. De Creator pulled us through all de rubbish him tried to throw at us.

DEN I SAW A VISION OF PITMAN BROWNE!

Dis wuzn't just a dream. I call dis a vision. By de way, I used to know Mr Browne long long time back from I wuz a child. Him used to give me sista piano lessons, and sometimes him come to de house fe look fe me Mom. In dis vision, I couldn't tink wat wuz de connexion between him an'me.

Wen me wake up, his presence was still strong in de room, and fe de next couple a'months I-an-I had dis urge to try an'link-up wid him. It hap-pened dat one Saturday mornin' while I wuz drivin' along Radford Road in Hyson Green, me decided to call in de Nile River Book Shop. Him wuz coming out a de back room Office. I immediately asked de Manager's per-mission to speak to Mr Browne. Afterwards, I invited Mr Browne in me car to tell im bout me dream, an' him wuz tellin' me 'bout him book.

"INKLINGS OF A BLACK CHRIST"
BY MR BROWNE!

Roydel; now envisioning a new life followed by a New Year's Resolution as he embarks on the threshold of the year 2000. Lisa is by his side.

Rasta? A tell Mr Browne every ting 'bout me dream, an Mr Browne tell me everyting' bout how him manage fe write him 'Inklings of a Black Christ' book. In de car we spend hours and hours talkin'. D'yu know sometin' Rasta? I-an-I man is amazed dat Mr Browne had de courage to write such a book. A start to tink of all de people like Steve Biko, Malcolm X, Marcus Garvey and all de powerful man and woman who did try fe reveal de same truth dat society did a try fe hide. Afta de conversation wuz finish, I asked Mr Browne if him would teach me some a de tings dem dat him write in dis book. Him agree fe we start fe meet every Friday at me Mom's. Him even start fe teach me fe write essays in Black History. Two years down de line, Mr Browne invite me fe write de Preface fe dis him 3rd book. I-an-I is very honoured dat him should ask me. New Year's Resolution before de year 2000, I man stop smokin' as a sacrifice before de Almighty Creator! No more weed!! I man finish wid dem tings. I-an-'I is a new man now. At firs' it wusn't easy-tanks an' praise to de Creator who did give me de strength. De majority a de tings I used to do, a put dem down to experience. Sizzla sey,"wen yu live an' yu learn, anyting' wrong yu do, yu get in return. Now I am a believa in faith. I live by faith. Faith is de key to our survival in dis oppressed society. And while I am on it, I keep tellin' Mr Browne dat de Spirit tell me, sey it is time fe me fe get baptize. I man is lookin forward to dis ere baptism.

Finally, just to close, I would like to say "One Love" to me Mom for standin' by me although I caused so much trouble. Also f'helpin' through the Resurrection process of me life. Also to the Creator for makin' all these things happen.

"ONE LOVE!" — Roydel 'Youth Man'

"NOW THAT I HAVE FOUND MY 'REAL' SELF, I WILL NEVER BE THE SAME!",

says Roydel 'Youth Man' Lothian of Nottingham.

I wish to continue an in-depth study of "Inklings of a Black Christ" by Pitman Browne.

I wish to study my bible and recognise the great contribution Black African People have made to it.

"Know Thyself!"
Maslow's theory

and develop my reading and writing skills...

No more teefin.
No more sellin crack.
No more selling cocaine.
No more smokin weed.

re-education
search for 'real' self

Sellin crack cocaine
Started to burgle houses
Started smoking black ash
Put into foster care
Started to teef monies from petty cash

ACKNOWLEDGEMENTS AS AMIABLY ENSHRINED WITHIN THE CONTEXT OF THESE PAGES.

By way of continued acknowledgement let me say
Peoples' College is no stranger in the sense that
its I.T. skills and learning resources facilities
have been of help not only
in the preparation of this book,
but during the course of my previous publications.

As such, this manuscript is giving me a chance
to put into practice
some of the things
I have learned.

And a mention also to Mr John Rudd, Principal of the College for kindly undertaking to write the Foreword.

PROOF READING

Let me say while I am on it, that the energy and skill required in proof-reading, can never ever be underestimated. The proof-reader is the detective who liaises with any Editor in order to ensure that no stone in relation to the written word remains unturned. Consequently, I am grateful to Lilieth Wade — Author of "Through Many Dangers" (1999) for assisting in this area.

Finally, I would like to allow a mention for Dennam Varcianna who has stepped-in at the eleventh hour to inspire the project with helpful advice on matters pertaining to marketing and distribution.

FROM THE NEW TESTAMENT CHURCH OF GOD!

Bishop George A. Beason

Also, a note of commendation for the much needed concern by way of prayerful devotion which is being shown and expressed by the Bishop of the New Testament Church at this time. Most sermons I hear him preach, appear to strike right at the heart of the family and its needs. The family, when saying so, lies at the very root of our community based institutions. And the advent of each divinely inspired message, brings with it, the inbuilt expression of a prayer that spells hope, pardon and peace.

As Editor of this book, I welcome Bishop Beason as he comes forward to pray for peace among our youths, peace among the factions which unfortunately have become more and more divisive over time, peace within their relative homesteads, peace on our streets, peace in terms of a genuine cessation to violence, peace in terms of a semblance of good will one towards another, and above all, peace with The Almighty, the Just Judge who respectively accords pardon, reconciliation and hope through Our Lord and Saviour Jesus Christ:

"Thank you Pitman Brown! Let me say how pleased I am to see the transition you are making as you continue to translate your thoughts into book form. And along with readers of this book, I want to congratulate the literary skills you are attractively displaying within the specialist vernacular of today's Self-Publisher. Through research procedure, <u>Pitman quite often provokes the wrath of the stereotypical, even well-held religious views. Out of controversy comes courage and defiance. In this sense he is willing to erect a monument of posterity for generations to follow, not only through the medium of his self-styled Performance — Poetry and Classical Piano Music, but now, through the instrumentality of his writing skills.</u>

At this juncture, let me take time out to reflect on our youth subculture, as this comes in line with the theme provided by this book:

My prayer goes up for those who through the disadvantages of peer pressure, are having to sacrifice their principles to end-up doing things they do not really want to do. My prayer goes up for those who are enslaved and encumbered by the inconveniences caused by a life of drugs. My prayer goes up for those who live in fear of drug-related violence. My prayer goes up for those who are cornered into the pressures of gang-related warfare. My prayer goes up for those who need a job Lord, but do not know where to turn. My prayer goes up for those who have turned their backs on the sheltered home life they once knew. Please Lord God, go into each individual heart and deal with each individual need.

Finally, as the Author has made mention in these pages of parents (notably 'Pegie Man' and Ruby) from our own St Ann's community who unfortunately have lost their sons in gang warfare: Please, be there for them Lord. Be thou a bulwark, a shield, an anchor and a restorer of the breach. Heavenly Father, thou knowest... thou knowest everything... Amen!"

THE YOUNGEST YOUTH MAN EVER!

My name is Theo Browne. I am six and I like to write a lot.

I also like to play on the computer.

I am glad to be in dad's book.

Writing by hand is slowly becoming a thing of the past; or, that's the way it seems at the moment. Theo, in all probability, is aiming to effect a general balance between the art of typing words on a computer, and the much older art of writing by hand. 'Once a writer, always a writer'!

Pitman Browne

YOUTH MAN EXPRESSES IT IN PENCIL DRAWING!

Paul Michael S. Berwise-Ebanks

21 year-old London based Paul helped to add lustre to my own attempts to disclose evidence of the existence of the human ghost (astral) body — (See p 62 of 'Wishing Can Be Dangerous').

Within the context of visionary life-drawing skills that seem to get better and better, I would once again like to take the privilege of saying 'welcome Paul to the pages of 'Children get out of the Ghetto Mentality'! If you turn to page 137, you will notice he is portraying the happy face of an imaginary girl from Nottingham called Myrna. Also, in turning to page 138 you will see his pencil drawing of the sad face of yet another imaginary girl called Marva.

More information on Paul:

Incidentally, he is quite a frequent contributor in terms of poetry and ingenious pencil drawings to a twice-yearly magazine called "WRITE SPARK". This magazine is the product of the Hackney Creative Group which meets every second Monday of the month at Stoke Newington Library, Church Street N16. Anyone wishing to get in touch with Paul, for pencil drawing related work, please contact Pitman Browne, Editor, through the e-mail address provided within these pages.

LET'S DEBATE REGGAE TO RAGGA AT KARIBU!

I am particularly grateful to the residents of Karibu Youth Hostel in Basford (Nott'm) for their co-operation throughout the course of an exciting debate on Ragga which as we all know, is an off-shoot of the Jamaica Reggae industry. The atmosphere was right... too right! From de whole a we, some nuff nuff chat wuz goin on; ya man. In the end, three came forward to pose in front of the camera. Jahlikah (right) takes the view that ragga is low in moral uplift-ment, and much too harsh:

"Ragga is not like beautiful songs. Ragga is too harsh. For the girls it can be a little off-putting... the lyrics an' that. I think Reggae is more softer... a bit like chill-out music".

Jason (left) responds by redressing the balance:

"Ragga is expressive. I don't say any of it is bad. It is the truth about ghetto conditions in real life; hardships, bad luck and pain".

Bakary (kneeling) came from the kitchen to join us. He definitely prefers Reggae. On a change of subject, he says:

"I like it here at the Karibu Hostel. It is a good mix between Black and White. I like discussions where it gives me a chance to share the culture of what African freedom fighters like Kwame Nkhrumah and Sekutore have accomplished".

For more on Karibu youths, see page 67

Spec 'B'
Performer-Poet, Singer-Songwriter, Graphic Design Artist and Photographer

Thanks also for the influence and expertise of a Nottingham based Artiste whose individual history has been characterised by a general involvement with schools workshops activities punctuated by the cut and thrust of life in the entertainment industry.

Spec 'B' has come along to give a lending hand to the pace and direction of an exciting debate which will bring this frank and honest book to the final pages of its conclusion. "THE GREAT GANJA DEBATE" is no pushover. If it is anything to do with valuable research information, you will perhaps comprehend the true extent of his own personal contribution — dare I say more!

ON MATTERS PERTAINING TO MENTAL HEALTH

Dr Chris Udenze of the St Ann's Health Centre

A word of welcome also to Dr Udenze who has kindly stepped into these pages to deal with the range of treatments on offer for those who are seeking general advice in the face of mentally related ills. Also, he will take on board the assumption that our Western Psychiatric model is often at fault when it comes to diagnosing African Caribbean people within the framework of a society which is by and large, racist. In point of fact, he advances the claim that on the premises of cultural understanding alone, people from time to time, are finding themselves wrongly labelled:

> "Nottingham is infamous for a survey which seems to show that more Black people have schizophrenia than Whites. Was it that White Psychiatrists were wrongly diagnosing Black patients when they were just responding to stresses in an extreme way?"

For instance, in this book, I have taken the opportunity of putting to the Dr my doubts about the role of anti-depressant drugs. Also, a number of anonymous persons have submitted articles questioning the usefulness of tablets like Prozac and Chlorpromazine or even Electro Convulsive — shock treatment — therapy. By reasoned argument alone, some appear to favour the view that counselling or meditation related treatments are far more beneficial propositions. Finally, while we are on the question of mental ills, let us spare a thought for those youths who unfortunately are confined to mental hospitals — thank you!

'Pegie Man' Robinson of St Ann's

62-year-old 'Pegie Man' was a youth during the Summer of 1958 when areas like Robin Hood Chase, and St Ann's Well Road were embroiled in running battles between Teddy Boys and West Indian youths particularly at nights after pubs were closed. Emerging from the level of advice I was given, I felt it would be in good accord for me to meet-up with him, just so I could come away with a fuller and clearer picture encapsulating his own viewpoint of what life was like in the Nottingham of more than 40 years ago.

With him, you can feel the language of the street... a language that is in him. Common sense all the way! When he tells a story, I find it very difficult to keep a straight face. Without my pencil and notebook — just imagine — all these wonderful experiences would have gone to waste! With him, never a dull moment.

As an ex-patriot Jamaican of Indian Maroon descent, he is especially appreciative of the history of the brave Shanty Warrior slaves who broke away from their ranks and joined-up with the Maroon Resistance Movement in the hills of Jamaica. Incidentally, he tends to describe our present youths in Hyson Green, Broxtowe, Sneinton, Meadows and St Ann's as:

"Sons and daughters of brave Shanty Warriors!"

In terms of actual blood line, he declares that he is the great-great-great-great — grandson of Nanny, the Warrior Queen of the Ashantis!

Photograph taken by Spec 'B'

Vanessa Graham
a St Ann's Sister of the Order of Rastafari

In terms of pockets of information and fields of thought, this sister is the most versatile and well-travelled of all I have so far approached for help in putting together this book. You will find as you follow through the various situations relating to youth subculture, that her evidence (as based either on what she has read, who she has met or which countries she has travelled) will strike an authentic and convincing note throughout the pages as you read.

For instance, take the claim she is advancing as she opens the "GREAT GANJA DEBATE": what she is saying in effect, is that unspoiled ganja from the natural earth does not harm anyone. She justifies this claim by drawing upon the confessions of a youth on ganja whilst being diagnosed by a Psychiatrist as mentally ill. This youth poured out his heart to Vanessa and told her all the social issues that were bothering him — in other words, it certainly wasn't the ganja that was responsible for ruining his life.

Also, with respect to cocaine and its mass influx in our community, she invites source evidence from "The Emperor Wears No Clothes" by Jack Herer (1993) to suggest that there is a racially motivated conspiracy to undermine Black people, and Intelligence agents like the C.I.A. and F.B.I. have deliberately been releasing cocaine in the American Ghettos since the 1960s

Photograph taken by Spec 'B'

Lorraine Mc Hale

Lorraine better known to her friends as Doreen, has been an instrumental source reference in the sense that the general content of these pages and even the title of the front cover — given the type of book I should try and aim for — came out of a series of advice suggestions which she gave me.

In this sense, Lorraine is no stranger. She has helped through sharing knowledge, sharing spiritual experience and offering spiritual guidance. She believes the Great Jehovah is her refuge and strength, and He is the one who is speaking through her as a channel of guidance.

In terms of drugs and health issues, she takes a good strong posture on the direction she thinks young people should be taking in today's world. Her anti-drug views seem to surface on those pages which are designed to reflect the youths at their weakest and most vulnerable.
Perhaps her best contribution throughout the whole book, comes from "THE GREAT GANJA DEBATE"! This is an exciting debate which will bring this frank and honest book to the final pages of its conclusion.

PROSTITUTE OUTREACH WORKERS

Also, I would like to take time out to say thank you to Susan Johnson (dressed in scarf) and her Staff at P.O.W. for helping to shed light on some of the issues as they unfold within the pages of this book.

In particular, I know there are some who have had support and advice at times when practical help was most needed. Incidentally, I have allowed a few of these 'thank you' (anonymous) letters to be featured within this book — see pages 122-124 and 129-132.

Should any reader be wishing to make contact with P.O.W. on a confidential basis, please do not hesitate to contact Pitman Browne, through the e-mail and telephone facilities of the editorial page, and I will pass on the details.

RACE RIOTS ST ANN'S 1958!
...and Manley came.

IN MEMORY OF
NORMAN WASHINGTON MANLEY, M.M., Q.C.
Patriot and Statesman

What did he say to the people of Nottingham?
Turn to page 45

CONTENTS

CONTENTS Continued

SHE RE-DISCOVERED HER' REAL' SELF

This is a Nottingham story as told by
another Youth Man known as 'Youth Man X':

Preface Part 2

"Something… just a little something to buy a cuppa tea please?"
"Sorry luv".
"Excuse me please, could yu-"
"Move out th'way… got to catch me bus!"
"Excuse me, could you spare me10 pence please?"
(Another passer-by nods: 'sorry duck… can't help!').
"Excuse me kind sir… … (Yet another rejection).
"O MY GAWD! GAWD WOT 'AVE I DONE? SOMEBODY? ANYBODY??
WOT 'AV I DONE TO DESERVE THIS???"
  (Her voice is drowned-out by the sound of three motor bikes, and the
crowds are moving faster as rain starts coming down). "O NO!!! ME
BELLY!!! O MY GAWD!!! I'M HUNGRY!!! !!!" .

'YOUTH MAN X' — the stranger — APPROACHING:

"Yow!" (She ignores him and walks away).
"Yu a get wet-up? Talk to me sista! Yu a rite?"
She stops; turns and looks at him. Her blue eyes are partly hidden by
wisps of blonde hair. She looks about 19.
  "Come out a de rain man; cum eenside Mac Donald's?", pleads the slim
brother sporting blue tam, short goaty beard and shoulder-length dread-
locked hair. He looks about 35.

Before I go any further, this is a true story. 'Youth Man X' came face to
face with a beggar who was literally planning to take her own life because
she could not stand the humiliation of begging. Three days of starvation
was enough. The sheer hell of living at home was even worse, that's why
she had to run away. After treating her to a meal at Mc Donald's, he gave
her pocket money and begged her not to take her own life because she had
a lot to live for. She should try and search for the 'real self' inside her.

Years later, she thanked him for saving her life. She is currently the Man-
ageress of a Restaurant in another town, and drives a Mercedes Benz. She
got out of her car and introduced him to all her friends, then disclosed her
address details, as well as a personal invite, in case he ever wished to take
up the offer of coming to spend a lovely holiday with her and friends.

FROM ANOTHER GIRL, A DESPARATE CRY FOR HELP !!

This is another true story as told by 'Youth Man X' of Nottingham:

About 3:o'clock on a sunny afternoon as 'Youth Man X heads towards the paper shop at the corner of a busy Nottingham street, he says "yow!" to a smiling African Caribbean girl sitting on a wall near the shop. On his way out of the shop he could sense a cry of help lurking behind her smile:
"Yu a rite sis?"
"Cha no!"a aven't eaten a thing all day".
"Yu kidding!"
"Cha no man, it's bad; help me wid a dinner noh man?"
"I man not seen you roun' dis area befor..."
"Cha no man, I come from outa town".
"Where about?"
"Newcastle".
"Really? Yu cum fram Newcastle?"
"Ya man; seriously, I 've never been so hungry for a long time'".
"Listn' right? Listen-up: I no gwine giv yu no money 'cause yu gwine tek me money go buy alcohol".
"No brother man shame, a wouldn't do such a thing; no man!".
"Yu eena drugs an dem kind a tings?"
"No man, honest".
"If yu cum wid me, I we kook you a meal owz at?"
"Ya man that's fine, that's cool".
"Yu trus me?"
"Ya man me trus yu".
"Cum den noh... me jus liv ova dey soh". (They start walking...)
"So wen did yu cum up fram Newcastle?"
"This morning man".
"Wah? YU JUS CUM DIS MAWNIN? AN NO 'AV NO MONEY? WHERE IS YU MONEY? YU NEVVA BRING ANY?"
"No man".
"Ow did you pay de train? Yu cum pan train or coach?"
"No man, me hitch-hike..."
"YU LIE! NO BLACK GAL NO HITCH-HIKE IN A BRITAIN".
"O please you've got to believe me (Tears welling up in her eyes... he takes the front door key out of his pocket then opens the door, and they both go inside a terraced house).

"All I had with me when I left Newcastle, was this plastic bag with one change of underclothes; nothing else.

PROSTITUTE EARNS 75 PENCE???

As she continues to brood over a cup of tea and biscuits, 'Youth Man X' puts on the rice, cuts up fresh vegetables, and takes out some pre-cooked curried chicken legs from the fridge freezer:

"My husband and I had a row... this time he went too far..."

"Him beat yu?"

"Yes, he beat me-up. Him beat me all the time. I kyp telling 'im he mustn't bring other men to share our bed with us at night, and he kyps doing it — "

"WAH? 'IM BRING MAN FE SLEEP WID YU?"

"And because a told him a didn't feel like it this time, he started slapping, punching and kicking me in front of his two White friends".

"AN' HIM CHUCK YU OUTSIDE?"

"No, I lef of me own free will. I decided, <u>come hell, come high water I wasn't going to stand for this any longer</u>. When I stormed out of our 5-bedroomed semi-detatched in Newcastle — "

"Big, big house: Yu jokin'?"

"<u>No man serious, we have swimming pool and a long long driveway with gardens on both sides plus two garages</u>. Late late 12 o'clock at night wen im beat me, I screamed and screamed... then run straight out of de house; One big slam from the heavy iron gates and I was gone".

"Sista, de cup dem small. You wouldda like anoder tea?"

"Go on then... So I waved a passing heavy goods lorry driver. Up front, I told him I would offer my services as a prostitute, even without payment, so long as he took me to whichever town or city he was going and would you believe it, we covered more than 60 miles to get to Stoke-on-Trent and he never touched me? <u>I kept thinking to myself 'this is the first time I had ever offered myself as a prostitute to anyone. It never worked. It was never meant to be</u>'. When I got out of the vehicle, I was hungry, tired and still penniless; so I started hitch-hiking with the hope that I would get a vehicle to take me to another town".

"Why Nottingham? Lawd sista! Yu get a rough, rough deal!!!"

"My biggest upset came when another heavy goods vehicle bound for Nottingham pulled up. We agreed my price plus how much would be deducted for payment of my fare to Nottingham.

But it wasn't to be. I knew it. All along, I could feel the virtue of what my 'higher self' was telling me — call it conscience if yu like".

"Sista yu speak sum very very good English dem! Dem whole heep a English good man! Been to Public School an all dat?".

"No not a chance. I went to the Poly before I moved to Newcastle. Nowadays they call it University. The lorry driver was as stubborn as an ox. The man blankly refused to open-up his pockets and hand over ma money. All it boiled down to, was abuse; that's the long and th'short and th'tall. He abused me. So when I arrived in Nottingham, —"

"Wat time yu cum?"

"Shortly after 6 this morning. I explained I didn't know anyone in this town yeah? Moreover, I was hungry and needed something to eat. All he offered me was the 75 pence which was rattling, and rattling, and rattling on the dashboard throughout the whole 50-mile journey from Stoke-on-Trent to Nottingham".

"DE MAN WANT SUM GOOD CLAP-UP!", said 'Youth Man X'.
"HYSON GREEN BWOY DEM GWINE GIV 'IM A CLAP-UP!"
"Come sista, cum! Cum we heet sum a de food noh?"
She is greeted by the sweet sweet overpowering aroma of hot food, as she gets up from out of the settee and joins him at the table. In the meantime she must be thinking:

Oh what hospitality!

Oh what a welcome!

Oh what a relief!

On the table mat he now places a hot pyrex dish full of white rice mixed-up with diced red peppers and sweet corn. Then another pyrex dish steaming with chicken legs enmeshed in curried gravy.

"Self-service yu see; grab dis plate an' so".

As they start eating, he exclaims:

"I WILL SEE DAT YU GET SOMEWHERE NICE TO — "

"To stay?"

"A hostel... nat far from ere. I liv wid de girl fren yu see".

"The girl friend?"

"An she is sensitive yu see... I av' a kid as well."

4

SEND HER ON THE STREETS?

"Boy or girl?"

"Girl".

"How old?"

"Ten...... you?

"I have three children; one nine, and two in their teens".

"Really?"

"YOU KNOW...YOU ARE ABOUT THE 4th MAN I HAVE MET SINCE COMING TO NOTTINGHAM THIS MORNING".

"Yes?"

"Yes!"

"Tel me bout de odder man dem".

"ALL A'THEM WANTED ME TO GO OUT ON TH' STREETS".

"Yu mean...(looking shocked) yu don't mean—-"

"TO WORK, YES; TO WORK TH' STREETS O' NOTTINGHAM. THEY WANTED ME TO EARN MONEY FA THEM".

"Right: right sista, a hear yu! Yu've seen th' good th' bad an' th' ugly".

"WELCOME TO TH' STREETS HA?!"

"Put it down to experience... Man's inhumanity to man".

"AND TO WOMEN AS WELL".

"I ave heard worse".

(AT this point, they are about to leave the house. Later that evening, Youth Man X succeeds in finding accommodation at a local hostel for women for her).

JUST A FOOT NOTE

To be honest, I don't quite know how this story ended. Youth Man X informed me that a dramatic phone call saved this woman from the worst. Few days later after she had settled into emergency accommodation for women, Social Workers as well as Police, tried to negotiate a re-union between her and her three children.

Dear readers:

This is the most moving story I have ever had to put into print. For any stretch of the imagination, this woman has seen men at their worst. Name it, she has been there; she has seen it all. She has seen men at their worst behaviour.

Youth Man X in rescuing her — giving her food and finding emergency accommodation in a hostel — has demonstrated a shining example of the 'real' self at work. In other words, don't despair! You will always find good men. They are not all bad you know? In the first place, it was the 'real' self that drove this woman to flee her children and her home to seek help. My message to any woman in difficulties is follow you instincts! Let the 'real' self come out. Nine cases out of ten, the 'real' self is never wrong.

5

INTRODUCTION:
TO
SOME
OF
THE
MAJOR
PROBLEMS
ENCOUNTERED
WHILST
RESEARCHING
THIS
BOOK:

"KNOW THY SELF"
by Abraham Maslow

Several persons have come up to me in the street and said: "Pitman Browne no, no, no you can't ascribe honour and glory to Abraham Maslow for a term he didn't create. How can you take an age old African phrase like 'know thy self' and apply it to a contemporary Western scholar like Maslow? For the sake of historic accuracy, 'know thyself' was actually translated into French and eventually English after Napoleon's soldiers found it inscribed on temple walls and ancient monuments during their notorious invasion of Egypt in the 1800s". Yes, yes, yes, I would not dare negate any of that. It would probably be unfair if I did — so let's continue this trend of thought:

Even the triangle which Maslow is using to convey his message, (as seen on the front cover of this book), is the product of African thought. The 'Osiran' triangle as it is appropriately called, originated from the oldest expression of the Holy Trinity on earth, and was meant to symbolise a pre-dynastic Black African family known as Isis (mother), Osiris (father) and Horus (the original Black Christ son born on 25th Dec) from the ancient Egyptian Religious Drama so that the actual triangle in symbolic terms was first used as a reference to these three people — see Stolen Legacy (1957) by George G.M. James.

'Know thy self', says Afro American George G.M. James in Stolen Legacy was not actually attributed to Greek thought since Socrates was himself a baptised and circumcised Initiate of the Black African Metaphysical School in Egypt. 'Know thy self' as taught by the Egyptian Priests, meant that we should try and acquire mastery over our passions! Once we had done that, then the various strands of our latent (buried) potentials would begin to blossom. Good memory is a wonderful inner gift: so is Clairaudience (or clear hearing) both in sleeping and waking states. Clairvoyance (or clear seeing) is another beautiful gift to acquire. These were gifts of SELF — KNOWLEDGE as taught by the ancient Egyptian Priests!

THE SELF-KNOWLEDGE TRIANGLE BY MASLOW

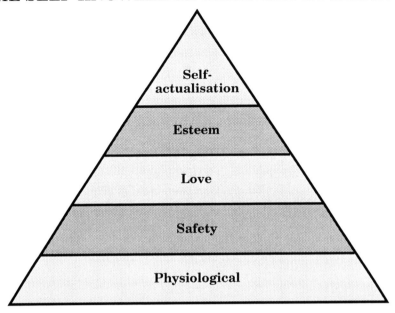

(Maslow's triangle as quoted from Management and Organisational Behaviour by Laurie Mullins through Pitman Publishing, 128 Long Acre, London WC2E 9AN, U.K.)

The 5-point principle which Maslow has constructed within the triangle, starts from the very base or lowest need — 'THE PHYSIOLOGICAL' which is the need for <u>food and sex</u>! In between is the need to feel safe — 'SAFETY NEEDS' — , social activities within social groups — i.e. 'LOVE NEEDS' and then 'ESTEEM NEEDS'. But at the very top of the triangle itself, you will find 'SELF-ACTUALISATION' which is the high point of Maslow's theory.

The 'SELF-ACTUALISATION' level, is the level which allows you to tune into your 'REAL' self! Your 'REAL' self tends to manifest itself in whatever potentials or natural gifts you have. Again, your 'REAL' self is the sum and substance of what you are worth as a person! He also maintains that the lower need areas are short-lived. Once needs like a bed, a bread and a roof over your head have been met, then you will automatically be wanting to find higher needs to replace the former needs.

One possible route to 'SELF-ACTUALISATION' is through re-education; not education, but re-education where you can learn to come to grips with <u>what you really want out of life</u>. Drama, and Music can help to bring one in touch with one's 'REAL' self!

THIS BOOK IS LITERALLY STRUGGLING TO FIND THE SORT OF 'HARD EVIDENCE' IT NEEDS!

The research requirement I have set, is very different from my previous two books. Whereas with them, I would be content to cross-reference from other authors, but with this one, I dare not. Life would just not look real enough. This book needs to be 'live' all the way through. It needs to be buzzing with the language of the street. To make it work, I need people to be talking with me about their joys, hang-ups and rock bottom experiences. This in essence, is the actual reason why the Preface is like a long, winding road full of frustration, yet counterbalanced by images of dramatic change. Pain in the sense that 'when you are down, there is only one way you can go, and that is up!' The Preface of this book to my mind, sums up the language of the street with a tinge of freshness and realism.

For this cause, I must ascribe special credit to Roydel Lothian ('Youth Man Roydel') for coming forward and sharing his thoughts in such a positive manner. Striking unbelievably at the very heart of courage itself, this Youth Man is courageous to the point of daring: For instance, he doesn't mind disclosing his name, or better still, a photo, so you can see who it is that's talking to ya! Nobody, (think of it) absolutely none of the featurers in these pages would probably have ventured to effect so convincing a level of self-examination within a book which general members of the public will now have access to read, share and discuss both in the here-and-now and many years to come!
Genuinely, one can understand if Youth Man X (the next in Preface Part 2) has specifically requested not to be identified by his 'real' name. As Author I should respect the privacy and anonymity of anyone who has hitherto requested it.

Finally, for those parents — Ruby and 'Pegie Man' — who have lost their sons in gang wars, I am honoured journalistically for the courage they have displayed whilst contemplating active roles within the confines of these pages. I am grateful to them both.

MY DIFFICULTIES WITH RESEARCHING THE UNDERLYING CAUSES OF THESE GANG WARS:

I am sick and tired of hearing about 'turf', 'gun', 'territory' and 'tit-for-tat' every time somebody gets shot in Nottingham. If I am in the queue at the Post Office, or waiting at the bus stop or simply just browsing through the papers inside a college canteen and ask somebody to come and give me some help with the manuscript for my book as I need to find out what is causing the gun-violence in St Ann's, you can bet I am going to end up with the same gibberish to do with:

"'turf', 'gun', 'territory' and 'tit-for-tat'!

People are willing to say:

"THIS IS THE WORK OF THE MEADOWS BOYS AGAIN. ALL THESE SHOOTINGS IN ST ANN'S ARE THE WORK OF THE MEADOWS BOYS..."

Yet when I ask them to come and be a part of my book, or stand up and substantiate what they are saying they won't. They may either close the discussion abruptly and run-off, or change the subject altogether. What does one understand by the phrase 'the language of the street? Could this be an example? If somebody knows something, the furthest it will ever get, is a rumour. A rumour is heresay and heresay can't go to law, so what do I do? Do I discount all the gibberish I'm hearing about Meadows boys this and Meadows boys that? O.K.! O.K.!! What do the Meadows boys want?

"THEY WANT TURF! THEY WANT TO BE ABLE TO CONTROL ALL THE TERRITORIES OF RADFORD, ST ANN'S, HYSON GREEN, SNEINTON AND SO FORTH".

This is the sort of thing I will hear. In fact, just to try and put everything into perspective, I occasionally stumble into those saying:

"RUBBISH! IT DOESN'T GO LIKE THAT AT ALL. IT'S THE ST ANN'S BOYS WHO ARE CARRYING OUT THEIR OWN THIS'N THAT TO MAKE IT LOOK LIKE THE FAULT OF THE MEAD-OWS BOYS, BECAUSE THEY ALL KNOW THE MEADOWS BOYS NEED SPACE TO SELL THEIR DRUGS".

In that case, I give up. I am right back to square one where I started. In the end it would seem my manuscript is woefully in need of HARD EVIDENCE. Where can I get HARD EVIDENCE from? If the youths of Hyson Green, Radford, Meadows and St Ann's won't talk to me on a realistic level, then I am not obliged to know the pains they are going through am I?

MUCH MORE OF A BREAKTHROUGH IN RELATION TO CITY GANG WAR ACTIVITY!!

During my research in this area, a number of possible scenarios were looked at in order to find the root of so-called gang warfare within Nottingham's youth subculture. The most plausible, so far, is the reasoning which describes the historical origin of territorial war — or fight — between youths living in the Meadows and St Ann's areas.

During the 60s, there was a club in the Meadows called Santa Fay. This club was frequented by Black guys from Radford, Sneinton, St Ann's and other parts of the city. They tended to merge in on this club in order to have a good night out — possibly to find a gal also. And speaking of gals, the White women in this club mainly came from the West Brigford end of town so more or less, it seemed the Meadows guys were controlling them.

The upshot of all this, is that fights between the Meadows guys and 'the outsiders' became quite common.

The Meadows set of guys, liked to feel they were boss! These guys — let's get it right — were not fighting over drugs. On the surface it might seem they were fighting over territory — turf. Deep down, there were differences between the Meadows and these so-called 'outsiders' from those early years. And such differences couldn't have amounted to much more than just bad vibes.

By the time it got to the 1980s, clubs like Santa Fee and Spider didn't exist anymore. Hence, the youths of Nottingham began concentrating their energies into football. As a matter of fact, there were teams like 'Clumber K and B', 'William Olds' and the Grasshoppers, so this sense of rivalry, continued in a sense though in a somewhat modified form.

The 1990s were faced with a situation whereby these football teams did not exist anymore…not in the same form at least since William Olds had now changed to the Cavaliers, and a new team — Forest Athletics — was now beginning to emerge on the scene.

The actual population of youths within the Meadows had undergone a dramatic increase during the 90s. Out of this population came three highly influential young guys known by their corporate street name 'The Big Three'! People say they virtually became professional in terms of small-scale house burglaries, High Street robberies and the drug scene. By now, lots of youngsters must've been equally eager to follow in their footsteps.

By the time 'The Big Three' got into Marcus Garvey to work on the door as Security, certain sections of the youth community had stopped going there for a night-out. Rightly or wrongly, they came to the conclusion that these guys were hell-bent on intimidating the rest of the Nottingham youth community, or hell-bent on getting their own back whichever way one might wish to take it!

In certain quarters, the view was entertained that <u>drugs was the underlying cause behind the type of gang wars that claimed the lives of Shane Thompson and Lloyd Robinson</u>. Both were savagely beaten to death during the 1990s! O.K. let's take crack-cocaine for a minute: crack-cocaine is a phenomenon of the 90s. It was getting off the ground in a very destructive way. Guys like The notorious Big Three were probably making nothing but some 'big' monies for the first time ever!

Still for all that, it would perhaps be wrong to drive one's self to the conclusion that drugs was the issue that brought rival gangs to a head. I am even advancing the view within the later pages of this book that 'money is the root of all evil' — hence, 'quick' money accruing from drugs must if anything, help to account for the greed, envy, suspicion and bad blood between rival factions dotted across the city belt. The deeper I plunge into such street-wise sources of information, the more I am convinced of the plausibility of undue apprehension and underlying tension, between rival gangs of youths in this city.

In the strictest sense, I would be reluctant to encourage anyone to take the view that Nottingham is expressly enmeshed within the throes of gang war activity... yet this is true in a sense.

For instance, just take a look at the Meadows geographically and judge the close proximity of Afro-Caribbean families living within the precincts of Bridgeway Hall right the way down to Bathley Street nr Trent Bridge: it would be relatively easy for one to come to the conclusion that Nottingham is dealing with a hefty strong gang of guys within a tightly-knit community.

This time, turn your eyes on St Ann's and you will see an altogether different geographical picture. For a start, St Ann's is so vast... Start with the bottom end of Ransom Road and worm your way through Robin Hood Chase all the way up to Woodborough Road and then Mapperley Road... what do we have? Certainly not a gang. We don't have gangs in St Ann's. What we appear to have is 'little crews' dotted over the vast expanse of territory — am I right?

These little crews tend to come together in pubs, clubs and on street corners mainly at night. They come together when they get a buzz out of the music. They come together to exchange information about this an'that. They might even come together if they wanted to set a — stolen — car on fire.

IS THERE A SOLUTION IN SIGHT?

Things — with the advent of the year 2000 on our hands — for the Meadows, have changed yet again: for instance, the 'Big Three' have now moved on. But the legacy of their influence is still left behind".
The real question, if any, takes the semblance of a 64-million dollar question which I couldn't wait to put to <u>one anonymous</u> <u>member of the public: Will there be an end in sight? Will there ever be a solution to the present trend of so-called gang war activity? Will there ever be an end to these shootings? For instance, will there be a truce at some point? Within the whole complex of youth groups is there a faction which is ready and willing to sit down and talk?</u>
"With Lloyd Robinson dead, and Shane Thompson dead what next? These are the precious sons of St Ann's soil. We have seen and we can read the anger that's written all over the faces of St Ann's youths. Still...... where there's a will there is hope. Yes, there are youths in St Ann's who would never ever sit down and hold any dialogue with Meadows. Having said this, this is not reason enough for not wanting to try and try and try until some kind of solution can be reached!"

The voice of the anonymous continues to ram home a few home truths:

"LISTEN TO ME: THE PARENTS! THEY HOLD THE KEY!! THIS MEADOWS AND ST ANN'S SITUATION HAS NOW GOT TO A POINT WHERE IT IS ONLY THE PARENTS WHO CAN SORT IT OUT. IF YOU CHECK THIS THING OUT, THE ST ANN'S AND MEADOWS PARENTS ARE FRIENDS. MOST OF THEM CAME TO BRITAIN IN THE 60s. MOST OF THEM SHARE THE SAME WORK PLACE AND EVEN THE SAME CHURCH. MOST OF THESE YOUTHS, WERE BORN IN THE 70s AND 80s .
WHENEVER THERE IS A KILLING, THE PARENTS TEND TO COME TOGETHER: WHY DON'T WE THIS? AND WHY DON'T WE THAT? AND THEN WHAT? THEY FIZZLE OUT AGAIN......

IF PARENTS FROM MEADOWS AND ST ANN'S SHOULD SET UP A COLLECTIVE WHERE THEY FUSE TOGETHER EVERY FORT-NIGHT AND EVERY MONTH, THE YOUTHS WOULD BEGIN TO LOSE THE WAR OF SEPARATION WHY?
BECAUSE OUR PARENTS ARE STRONGER THAN US!!!
AFTER THE KILLING OF LLOYD AND SHANE, GRAFFITI WAS FOUND WRITTEN ON A WALL IN THE MEADOWS. IT READ: 'StAnn's:2:Meadows: nil'.

THE POLICE CAN'T DEAL WITH THIS MATTER. THEY HAVEN'T GOT A CLUE. POLICE DON'T PRAY; ONLY OUR PARENTS WILL PRAY!!!".WHEN THE POLICE WILL ACT AGAINST US OUR PAR-ENTS WILL ACT IN OUR INTERESTS BECAUSE THEY LOVE US, NO MATTER WHAT.

REALITY

Killing our best crops
With Coke and Crack'
Our future resources turning to dust
Cutting... Shooting... Robbing and such
Black-mailing... Looting... Burgalising'
Don't you think that's a bit much?

Man owes them money'
Dem beat him and stab him
Till him drop, and guess what?
Dem a use guns as props
A go free too, all a that,
That is what that's being said
Him was too sick to get out of bed,
By the time him reach a doctor'
The poor man was already dead:

Wasting our youths once again'
Selling your Shit, your Cocaine,
Our future resources turning to dust,
Cutting... Shooting... Robbing and such
Black-mailing... Looting... Burgalising,
Don't you think that's a bit much?

Heroin abounding, causing all these killings,
Big cars a driving, Mobile phones a boasting,
Pretty clothes and Gold a modl'ing;
Our future resources turning to dust;
Cutting... Shooting... Robbing and such
Black-mailing... Looting... Burgalising,
Don't you think that's a bit much?

By Spec 'B'
21:11:90

PARENTS
WHO
HAVE
LOST
THEIR
SONS
IN
GANG
WARS
IN
NOTTINGHAM

IN AN INTERVIEW WITH THE MOTHER
OF SHANE THOMPSON

I am perplexed... worried... why? I am afraid I will have to be more honest with myself. In theory, perhaps I should be saying how very deeply
honoured I am to be talking to Ruby about a family tragedy which we all
feel. In practice, I feel embarrassed to say the least, since I am just a single strand enmeshed within the semblance of a caring and compassion-
ate community. Whatever it is that parents are feeling at this time, I am
feeling it too. At one time, Shane Thompson was an active participant in
the general life of St Ann's. Ruby, in essence, has kindly allowed me the
privilege of visiting her house to effect and engage an interview which
will be featured within the pages of this book.

Please understand me when I say to the whole community that this
interview with Ruby, is not designed to attack the conscience of anyone.
What it is effectively designed to do in principle, is to give Ruby a chance
to say anything she wishes to say. When saying so, there are things she
might just not wish to share at all. General members of the public must
understand that her journey is no more, no less than a personal walk...
this is her path, and this is life as she sees it.

Finally, just before the interview gets under way, let me take time out to
say I have also spoken briefly with Shane's Father; this interview
nonetheless, will be a reflection of Ruby's own thoughts. I am sure that
many of the points she is making, will perhaps reflect near enough to
what he himself is thinking.

At home, she looks ever so well-rested as she lays back in a modern front
room settee which rocks from side to side...now and then she might say
a few words. The window is half-opened so she can get some fresh air.
With pencil in hand, I propose to jot down anything she says; hence, in
somewhat subdued tone of voice, I herewith proceed with my first question:

"Is there any justice?"

"No...... no justice at all...... Up till now, nobody has been sent down
for my son's murder".

"How old was he when he died?"

"Shane was 19".

"Was he the eldest or youngest?"

"He was the youngest of three".

"Did he manage to say any last words to you?"

"Hardly; he was out most of the time... in fact, I hadn't seen him for a few days. Mind you, I saw him briefly on the Saturday evening before his death".

"What date was that?"

"Saturday 30th November".

"What year was that?"

"1997; 3 years ago". (Her language at this point, is beginning to sound poetic as she pictured the last time she saw her son):

"It was rainy and windy. The leaves were blowing off the trees. It was wet and cold, I'll never forget". (She has a graceful look. Her head is bowed as if in deep thought... now and then, there is an occasional glance at the ceiling).

"He was driving past in a car. His friend must have nudged him, 'O look, there's your Mum', so he brake sharply:

"Hi Mum?"

"Why haven't you been round?", I asked.

"I'll come and check you later right", he replied.

"All that was going through my mind, was the way he was driving fast. The road was wet and slippery. When he drove-off I thought what if the car pulled-up too sharply at the corner of Cranmer Street and Mapperley Road? 'He was going too fast'... that's all I was thinking...... and then...... he looked so different. He had a black hat on his head. He looked changed. His face didn't look the same".

"You said you hadn't seen him for quite a few days; does he normally stay away for so long?"

"Well this is it you see Pitman; Shane doesn't normally stay away so long. When he is not spending time with his girl friend and adopted daughter, he is always with me. This time he stayed away for days, and I couldn't understand why??? It's as though something was drawing him away from me...... I could feel it".

"So O.K., Shane was a 19 year-old; was he playful?"

"O yes, Shane was playful and pleasant";

"And something about him began to change in his final days?"

"He liked to squeeze my arms and pull my hands; he liked to pinch me".

(O gosh, I wanted to ask her about Shane's death, but I couldn't bring myself to come straight out with it).

"When did you first hear of Shane's death?"

"He was on life-support machine before he died. Marva is Shane's Auntie. She and other family members came round during the early hours of the following morning to tell me".

"So...... what did they tell you?"

"That he was in a fight three times".

"Three times, please Lord no!"

"Yes. According to how I had it, he was involved in a fight three times that evening, and the final fight was the one that finished him off. It took place across the street from the pub. More or less, this was what they heard". (At this point, I give her time... just a little time to gather her thoughts... she quickly glances at the ceiling before bowing her head once again in reflection).

"Also... ... I heard from another source, that he was attacked by six guys... ... you know... ... Pitman?... ... my Uncle died recently... ... then my Mum died... ... I wasn't even well at the time...... right now I am on blood pressure tablets for life".

"So... ... you said this situation took its course on the same Saturday after you saw him. What time on Saturday night did this happen?

"I should imagine some time between 12:00 and 1:00 a.m.".

"Oddly enough, that same night before I went to bed I started saying my prayers. I don't do that very often, but I felt like saying my prayers that night. Also... I went to bed very late because I was watching two Vampire Horror films".

"Anything else?"

"Yes; even before I finished my prayers, I felt a 'strange' kind of presence in the room... ... a 'strange' energy hovering over my head. I didn't know what this was all about, but I can remember trying to fan it away and stop it hovering over my head; 'Get away from me'! I snapped".

"Really: how extra-ordinary"!

"After family members came and alerted me, I went to the hospital; by this time, they had already performed an emergency operation and put him on life-support machine to see if they could save him. As day progressed hour by hour, it wasn't, only a matter of dealing with Police, but there was this whole business of having to make statements to the Press and frankly, I wasn't in any mood to talk to any of them".

"I listened to Shane's father on several news channels, (both TV and Radio), and I think he handled the whole thing quite well".

"As I see it Pitman, we were young once. We used to be young... well! Well!!... what a mess!!!... ... the mess of trying to sort out who did what to who!!!!"

I COULD NOT BELIEVE IT WAS MY OWN BLACK PEOPLE
— Ruby

"No I could not... At first, I thought this was probably the work of evil hands from some unknown place. In fact, I insisted it was the work of guys from outa town, I just couldn't believe, no I could not believe it was my own people! When it happened, they ran and hid. None of the youths involved in that awful tragedy came forward to try and explain what happened. It took three weeks of rigorous door-to-door Police work before anybody was brought in for questioning. They stayed away, or you might put it another way — they vanished from off the face of the earth without a trace".

"Yeah it's difficult", (my voice becoming even more subdued as she continues to unfold her thoughts, fears and feelings).

"That kind of death was not like when you die in a car crash".
"No... ..."

"I questioned myself... ... the way it happened: his neck was broke, they stepped upon his face, his rib was broke, two of his fingers had gone, his nose was broke and training shoes marks were left on the side of his face. This made me think... ... You know: They used to call upon me to help with the catering up at ACNA. Whenever there was a funeral, I didn't think twice; I went straight up and helped, especially if they asked. Who would have thought that my own son –mind you! Those caterers... ... they do a great job you know... ... eventually, it turned out that they had to cater for my own son".

"I was trying to keep-up with information especially to do with funeral arrangements. Rather, it was unfortunate that I missed-out on the actual day of the funeral; it must've taken a long time for Police to release his body for burial".

"Yes; it took 6 months before they released his body: Shane died on the 31 November, 1997, and was laid to rest on the 1st May 1998".

"Was there anything in particular that was going through your mind on the day of the funeral?"

"I felt hollow inside... I felt a kind of emptiness as soon as the hearse arrived... mind you, I did experience a sense of community spirit when I saw the whole volume of crowds that turned-out".

"Is there anything particularly of importance that you would like to say about Shane just before the interview is terminated?

"Two things: Shane is a very dedicated person; You ought to see the way he takes time out with his little adopted daughter. She was his love; all the time he would take her to the shops, and buy presents for her; he was that kind of person.

The other thing I would like to say about my son, is he was never given into drugs...he was not that kind of person...I want to make that clear!"

"Finally Ruby, I wish to end on the same note on which I started...'is there any justice?' — this was my question! Let me congratulate you for the courageous way you have shared your thoughts, not just with me, but I know there are readers out there who will relate very deeply to what you are saying in this book — the Lord bless!

LLOYD ROBINSON IS GONE
TO A BETTER PLACE!

It was well past midnight on the 4th August, 1993 when Lloyd, the 21-year-old son of 'Pegie Man' Robinson was involved in bitter confrontation with a gang of youths armed with baseball bats. Like the removal of Shane Thompson, this 'killer instinct' seems to rear its ugly head during the dead of night when all the people of St Ann's are asleep in their beds. One informed source claimed that Lloyd was trying to forge a settlement — albeit make peace — between rival factions from St Ann's and the Meadows. Unfortunately, it got out of hand when he got clubbed to death under the battering rams of a savage baseball bat.

'Pegie Man' saw it with his own eyes; this was after a caller suddenly knocked him up out of bed telling him his son was in trouble with Meadows boys; so he ran out in the street in his slippers and pyjamas:

> "**ONE ALMIGHTY LICK!!** My son was hit so hard it sounded like a drum".

"Pegie Man literally sank to his knees in utter disbelief with his own body shivering and shaking like an earthquake. He literally rolled up like a ball and bowed his head.

The sight of his own son was too much... not even time to say 'Lord have mercy' — **ONE BASEBALL BAT** — that's all it took!!! !!! !!!

What was so wierd about his death is, it took place within the radius of his family home, not far from his own gate... not far from the entrance to the ACNA Centre.

Earlier that Sunday evening, there was a christening party in the Centre. One source claimed Lloyd was acting as a go-between as two factions of youths were locked in a quarrel from in the afternoon. According to 'Pegie Man', the youths went away. Then later, they decided to come back and finish the argument.

> **"People say to me I should kill and take vengance fe de death of me own son. I bleed blood. You bleed blood. I must stand and give an account before my Maker and Creator. Killing brother, killing cousin, killing uncle is not going to solve any problem. So help me; I don't want no curse fe fall on me.**

My son died on the 4th August 1993. He was buried on the 1st September. Wen police came to my house fe tek statement, one of the parents of de youths was sitting at table wid me.

"I have never seen 2 people sit down in a murder situation and discuss it over a dining table. Never yet, have I seen this. Mr Robinson", mumbling with an undertone of sadness, "you are a very sensible man"!

Never, in all my 30-odd years in St Ann's have I seen a funeral like Lloyd Robinson's! The first of September was like a hot summers day. It was set for the afternoon and by mid-day, crowds had started milling round the precincts of the Mansfield Road Baptist Church. The older residents of the community who wanted to find a seat — everyone was struggling for space — made sure they arrived well before time. But the youth population my goodness, they were another story altogether. They were happy to hang around the sides of the church in little groups and little cliques. It seemed they knew the body would be escorted to church on horse-drawn carriage, so they stood around waiting... ... they were waiting for Lloyd to arrive.

As crowds continued converging on the church, I could see faces of youths whom I would not normally have associated with church at all. Or may be, they used to go to the Sunday School years ago to learn about 'Jesus Loves Me This I Know, For the Bible Tells Me So', but those days were over.

Inside the church itself, the solemn sounds of music from the pipe organ continued to paint the atmosphere as people waited. By now I was actually quite lucky to get myself a seat. My Word, I'll never forget the acclamation from the Minister:

"All rise!!! 'I AM THE RESURRECTION AND THE LIFE! HE THAT BELIEVETH IN ME THOUGH YE WERE DEAD, YET SHALL HE LIVE!'"

The coffin was slowly borne on the shoulders of the whole of the men from the Robinson's family. The funeral undertakers walked in front of the cortege and waited near the alter; they then took over from the Pall Bearers. By now, all of the overflow in respect of outside crowds, were literally crammed within every conceivable inch of space inside. The per-

24

sonality of Lloyd seemed to come out as sentiments of love and affection ring out amidst the atmosphere of a warm thanksgiving service. When it came to 'Abide With Me', people sang! They just let their feelings go. Incidentally, the long, and the short and the tall was this: LLOYD WAS LOVED. PARTICULARLY FOR THOSE YOUTHS, HE WAS SOME-THING OF A BEACON IN THEIR LIVES, OR A 'FEATHER IN THEIR CAPS' SO TO SPEAK.

<u>An added note on Shane Thompson's 'send-off':</u>

It really was a pity I missed out on Shane's funeral, despite loads of enquiries beforehand. By the time information reached me, it was days late. Or maybe it wasn't to be. I am rather like my Mom in the sense that I scarcely ever miss a funeral unless I could help it. Judging by what I saw of Lloyd's funeral, I should imagine Shane was given pretty much the same sort of warm characteristic 'send-off. When it comes to a show of strength, these youths in St Ann's are unbeatable! No rain, or fog or snow could ever have stopped them turning-out to a funeral such as this. Shane and Lloyd have no doubt touched the hearts of many — well? That's the way it is. We pass this way but once......

SHANTY WARRIORS
'Pegie Man' Robinson
Great great-great-great-great grand son of Nanny, the superb indomitable Warrior Queen of the Ashantis.

"THESE ARE SONS AND DAUGHTERS OF BRAVE SHANTY WARRIORS!"!

St Ann's man 'Pegie Man' Robinson, ex-patriot of Jamaica since 1957, says these Black youths are descendants of 100 of the bravest shanty warrior slaves who embarked from Captain Bligh's ship 'Bounty' as it landed in Jamacia during the time of the notorious Middle Passage. when slaves were taken from the Ashanti port of Ghana, West Africa.

All through the voyage they endured starvation except for drinking water, and when they landed, they made breadfruit their staple diet. The breadfruit plant incidentally, was brought on the same ship and introduced to Jamaica by Captain Bligh.

Kwame, a Nottingham based Sunday afternoon Radio broadcaster and Historian hailing from the Ashanti tribe, says 80% of Jamaicans are in fact Ashantis. Some African Historians will contend none the less, that the majority of Jamaicans are of Nigerian Yoruba tribal descent. They maintain that both Yoruba and Ashanti tribes were meshed in within a cross-section of other tribes, at the notorious slave port in Ghana (called the port of Goree Island), and it was from there that they were taken by ships and transported to the various parts of the Western world.

No Afrocentric researcher would dare undermine the bravery of Ashanti warriors like Nanny and her brother Cudjoe who on arrival to Jamaica, made good their escape with other slaves to lead the Maroon resistance in the mountains. Kwame says the Ashantis in the face of several British incursions into Africa have never ever been defeated, which ties in very well with what 'Pegie Man' is saying. In fact a little section of Kingston,

26

the capital city of Jamaica, is known as 'Shanty' town.

The descendants of these proud 'shanty' warriors (according to Trinidadian Historian, C.L.R.James), still maintain a strong anti-colonialist culture in today's world:

- They have their own anti-colonialist dub poetry.

- They have their own anti-colonialist dance to the rhythm of the drum beat.

- They have their own anti-colonialist lyrics.

- They have their own anti-colonialist political perception of Africa as their Mother Land.

- Their spirits in other words, will never ever be broken!

Kwame — A local Radio Broadcaster and African Historian

"LET US ENDEAVOUR TO STRIKE OUR ROOTS INTO THEIR (The Africans) SOIL BY THE GRADUAL INTRODUCTION AND ESTABLISHMENT OF OUR OWN PRINCIPLES AND OPINIONS, OF OUR LAWS, INSTITUTIONS AND MANNERS; ABOVE ALL, AS THE SOURCE OF EVERY OTHER IMPROVEMENT OF OUR RELIGION, AND CONSEQUENTLY, OF OUR MORALS".

by William Wilberforce
(The supposed "Liberator" of Africans from slavery)

This man is made out by caucasian historians to be supposed "Liberator" of African people from slavery. This is yet another lie in the propaganda war between the lies as told by European/caucasians, and the truth as told from an African viewpoint.

Wilberforce did nothing to emancipate the Africans from slavery. It was the sheer grit, courage, determination and desire of Africans to be free of the most uncivilised, barbaric, brutal system ever imposed on people that emancipated the Africans from slavery. The revolts of the Maroons, Nanny and Cudjoe in Jamaica, Harriet Tubman and Federick Douglas in North America and Jonathan Strong and Olauduah Equaino in England played a major part in the abolition of slavery.

Consequently, it would seem shameful if all of us stood back and allowed false information about Wilberforce to continue to flourish into our schools up and down the country.

The above speech which is not revealed by caucasian historians in a bid to hide the truth, shows the true extent of Wilberforce's hatred for African people. This speech just shows us as African people, how the caucasians have destroyed our communities hence, our very existence! This quotation helps to demonstrate the kind of colonisation, racism and oppression which continue to make its mark in ways that are covert, secretive and subtle thus destroying the very fabric of African people. As a result of this systematic programming, we the African-Caribbean youths –not forgetting our parents — have actually internalised it for instance in:

- A lack of respect for our elders.

- A lack of self-respect engendered in terms of Black male and Black female relationships and

- Black and Black violence in terms of the gang wars between Meadows, Sneinton, Radford and St Ann's.

Finally, I feel that this speech by Wilberforce will continue to do immense damage if we continue to be in a state of mental slavery. May I take the privilege here and now of wishing the Author of this book (and others like him) all the best in their endeavours to uncover the Afrikan-centred values that have long been rendered divorced from our being.

"THE REASON I USE THE TERM CAUCASIAN" — Kwame

The reason I never use the term 'white' — people — but 'caucasian', is because there is no such term as a 'white' race. African historical researchers like Chekh Anta Diop, Louis Leaky and Jorge A. Rogers have indicated that those who call themselves 'white', came from an area in Southern Russia called the Caucasas mountains. To be truthful, they were not even the aboriginees of Europe. These researchers maintain that the true European aborigines are the Grimaldis of Southern Africa who are in effect responsible for creating the Stone Age of Europe and Asia.

Supporting this, there is a famous Stone Age statue called the Venus of Willendorf which is to be found in the Museum of Human Sciences at Monaco near Monte Carlo, and the thick lips, broad nose, high breasts and big buttocks enshrined in its outline, are features which help to tell the story of an African presence in Europe as late as 12 thousand years ago. Willendorf, by the way, is a town in Austria. How could the original inhabitants of Europe carve a Venus so highly representative of Africans? This certainly is a question for Europeans to answer. Diop has also uncovered evidence of mass graves of early Stone Age Black Africans who lived in Europe and Asia. All this preceded the advent of the Great Ice Age. Before the Ice age, the climate was tropical. Once the ice age came, the original inhabitants progressively lost their pigmentation over a 200,000-year period (See "African Origins of Civilisation/ Myth or Reality" 1974 by Diop).

Afrocentric historians tell us that the caucasian people migrated westwards from the caucasas mountains through to the Balkans, thus settling in what is now known as Europe. The rightful term for our present Europeans is 'caucasians', because it correctly describes who they are and where they came from. The term 'white' is a misnomer. Other books helping to clarify this are, "The African Presence in Early Europe" (1989), by Ivan Van Sertima, and "The Black Man of the Nile and his Family" (1981) by Dr Yosef Ben-Jochannan.

RACE

RIOTS

IN

ST.

ANN'S

1958

RACE RIOTS IN ST ANN'S DURING 1958

A Nottingham Evening Post report dated 1st June, 1998, cited Saturday 23 August, 1958 as decidedly 'the worst night of rioting in the streets of St Ann's' when some 1,500 Black and White people armed with knives, milk bottles, knuckle dusters, bicycle chains, daggers, wooden planks, — not forgetting hand-to-hand fist-fights, resulting in ugly scenes of blood-shed, as well as some 8 hospital emergency casualties and 24 arrests. According to "Windrush" (1998) by Mike and Trevor Phillips, an incident started in a pub called 'The St Ann's Well Inn' on the Saturday night 23 August. A well-known ex-patriot Jamaican youth whose street name is 'Cain' was living at 18 Robin Hood Chase at the time, — incidentally, Cain now in his 70s, states that it was a pub fight that triggered the riot, and the actual pub was situated at Peas Hill Road nr Robin Hood Chase. Let me try and put in my own words, the sequence of events as Cain understands it to be:

"A Jamaican guy called David was sitting in the pub having his quiet drink, minding his own business when in walked an English girl. He greeted her. In little or no time they got talking, and then he bought her a drink. As one might have had it, she graciously accepted, so they carried on drinking and talking when in walked two Irish men. 'Get away from me...get away you Black bastard,' exclaimed the girl. The men immediately took issue with David. Two English men joined in and the atmosphere sky-rocketed into shouts and taunts and jeers and sneers and threats..."

At this point, it would be fair to incorporate another viewpoint which states that that there were sporadic outbreaks of violence inside the Lacarno Ballroom (now the Gala Bingo Club) between Afro — Caribbean youths and Teddy Boys on the very same night of Sat 23 August and 'Pegie Man ' Robinson provides source evidence of this, since he and a whole group of Black youths were on the dance floor at the time;

"Sey dem a cum wid bicycle chain fe lick we. I man 'av me ratchet een a my pocket right star? Teddy Bwoy dem nevva want we fe go een a de club. Dem did tink sey we a go tek wey dem Wyte gal".

'Pegie Man' believes there was also another Jamaican guy involved in the 'St Ann's Well Inn' pub. His name was Mick. To get back to what 'Cain' was saying, a fight broke out:

"Bystanders got involved in the kicking and thumping and punching amidst all the name-callings under the sun... 'you wot's it wot's it, get back to wherever'... so that beer glasses were sailing through the air and chairs hurling as missiles. 10:30 closing time could only have meant one thing: the pub doors had to be shut, so the fight naturally spilled over in the street. Whilst on the pavements it began to attract two types of crowds: one lot from the surrounding pubs and another lot from the houses in and around the Robin Hood Chase and Peas Hill area. Most of them were armed with knives, milk bottles, planks of wood and all sorts of weapons".

According to "Windrush" (1998) by Mike and Trevor Phillips,

"News of the fight spread like wild fire, and in a short time, a mostly White crowd of about 1,500 had gathered and started attacking Black people at random". (see page 169)

'Pegie Man's eyes went wild with rage as his mind went back to that awful Saturday night of nearly 40 years ago:

"Wen weee hear de news? a tel yu star: DEATH BEFORE DIS-HONOUR if I lie I die!!"

He throws his cap on the floor and clenches his fist in defiance:

"Wen wee hear sey dem a beat Black Man, de whole a we! 20 a we!! De whole a we!!! We ha fe fight we way true de crowd fe cum outside. De whole a we couldn't go pack-up een a Missa Gayle car fe go a Peas ill rode.
Some a de bwoy dem run fasta dan de car.
Melvin Downs, Alvin Mc Kenzie, Sonny Bravo, Doctor Bird, Eric 'Doons' Man, Bredda Doogie, Remel Smith, Cock Topie, Chick, Duggie, Chalkie and Pretty... me sey... ... DEATH BEFORE DIS-HONOUR if I lie I die!!!"

The reason these Black youths were literally faced with taking the law into their own hands (as stated by Mike and Trevor Phillips in "Windrush" page 167), was owing to the potential lack of faith they had in the Police system:

> "A lone Black man late at night was a safe target, because even if the Police got involved, they were likely to treat such affairs as routine faction fights".

The rhetoric of 'Pegie Man' Robinson peradventure will go some way to explaining the utmost significance of what solidarity amongst a minority group must have meant in those days:

> **"Dese youths of today... dese youths of Meadows, Hyson Green an' St Ann's don't know anyting... We ha fe fight! If we nevva fight fe dem in de early years, dem wouldn't able fe eat gravy from de gravy train. I speak to dem. I show dem wat de bad can bring".**

THE PROMINENCE OF
ROBIN HOOD CHASE!

When regular news bulletins and updates on the riot was relayed to Jamaica through BBC World Service Radio, I was only a 10-year-old. What struck me was 'why ROBIN HOOD CHASE'? No mention was ever made of Peas Hill Road, no mention of any pub, no, it was ROBIN HOOD CHASE all the way!!! I can even remember my Mum saying:

"Lord have mercy on my sister; She lives right in the heart of Robin Hood Chase".

Funnily enough, John Wray, my mother's sister's son — my cousin — was actually living in Robin Hood Chase at the time of the conflict. In fact, he had this to say:

"1958 when the riot took place, was the actual year I arrived in Nottingham from Jamaica. Robin Hood Chase was the place where I first went to live. 'The Chase' as they used to call it, was a central area connected with the conflict. At the time I asked the question 'why'.(?) Why was it that this time and place was chosen for this inglorious chapter of Nottingham's History?"

John, presently resides in Jamaica; he will perhaps be best remembered as a Teacher at Morley Junior in St Ann's between the 70s and 80s. He was also actively preoccupied with the team of Teachers at the Mundella Centre in the Meadows.

And speaking of that "inglorious chapter" — just to borrow a phrase from John — it is with regret that Nottingham's name had had to come to the forefront in the way it did. Several independent observers have gone on record as saying that the conflict that was staged at Robin Hood Chase helped in no uncertain terms to fuel the ensuing race riots that engulfed Notting Hill and the whole of the Ladbroke Grove area of North-West London! For instance, this is what a Nottingham Evening Post article (1/6/98) had to say:

"Soon the Notting Dale area now part of Notting Hill, was in flames with riots and street battles on a much larger and more violent scale than events in Nottingham.

The Nottingham riot succeeded in putting Nottingham on the map in the wrong sense".

Here, I will also have to try and question the role of the newspapers in the light of it's overall standpoint: for instance, whose side were they on? Mr Manley Taylor an ex-patriot Jamaican living in Nottingham during these conflicts, takes the view that the newspapers were unsympathetic to West Indians. The standard view, was that the West Inians were to blame for these disturbances.
Mr Oscar Reid, another ex-patriot Jamaican around at the time, takes the view that the Nottingham riot of 23 August, 1958, was sensationalised and overplayed by the press. On the one hand they were prone to ascribe blame 'fairly and squarely' at the door of the West Indians:

"**Blame for what? These people wouldn't even know a riot if they saw one. O'right let's stick with the Nottingham riot now: How many died? Go on, how many died? (to be truthful, I Pitman Browne couldn't answer because I wasn't there).**
Secondly, they talk about Black Man can't go dis place on him own... can't go dat place on him own because of Teddy Boy dis an Teddy Boy dat... I was able to go 'bout me business... Anytime me ready, I gawn... nobody no bother me. Now whose fault is that? De press hinny? A dem a mek de trouble".
Another thing you must try and understand is this: there must have been White people in dis country who were on the side of the Blacks, else dem would a kill de whole a we! The newspapers are the ones creating the hate..."

Mr Leonard Lawes now 92 and has lived in the Meadows during the time of the Nottingham and Notting Hill race riots. Whilst speaking with him in a local Nursing Home, I had to admit wow, maaan, this guy has got some really vivid memories and insights into the riots. First of all, he assured me that rioting in the streets of Nottingham were not just confined to the disturbances displayed on the night of the 23rd: rioting in effect, was spread over several weeks, both the weeks before and after the dreadful night of August 23, 1958. At the time, he had a well-known street name:

"Yes man! A me dem call 'She Mule'".

I asked him how he managed to get the name 'She Mule'. He has vivid memories of regular card games he used to play at the Cricketers Arms in the Meadows. Before the start of each game, he would challenge the rest of the players :

"If I lose, a mek she-mule breed tonight!"

Meaning, he would literally make the impossible possible — so confident was he that he was going to win! Everybody knows that a she mule can't give birth to a cub since a mule is masculine through and through. But this man liked to be dramatic. And surely enough, he was when it came to the business of street fights.

"De ting is dis: me did andastan' exactly 'ow fe deal wid de Teddy Bwoy dem. Mee no joke. A bad, bad man dis ya! Me always 'av me knife een a me' pocket... I don't mess".

This brother gave graphic details of street fights in which he was involved after 10:30 when pubs were closed. When it came to appearances in court he usually got away when the implications of self-defence were fully explained. A popular venue he remembers during the 1950s, was the Yates Wine Bar in Nottingham's city centre. This place became a great meeting place for West Indian men both from the Meadows and St Ann's area.

WHAT WERE THE IMMEDIATE CAUSES OF THE RIOTS?

The Nottingham Evening Post article dated 1, June 1998 cites racial discrimination in employment as an immediate underlying cause. In fact, political activist George Powe who helped found the St Ann's Afro Caribbean Artistic Centre (ACNA) is quoted in the same paper as saying that the employment situation amongst West Indians at the time of the riots was very bad:

> "The riot publicly exposed Nottingham's racial problems, forcing matters of discrimination in employment to come into the open for the first time... what we were saying was, 'if you had the qualifications, you should get the job like anybody else'".

Mr Oscar Reid, an ex-patriot Jamaican who was around at the time, told me there were only two firms in Nottinghamshire employing African Caribbean people i.e. Royal Ordinance Factory at Chilwell and an iron foundry in Beeston called 'Beeston Boilers'. 'Pretty', a Nottingham-based Jamaican ex-patriot now in his 70s is famous for turning the peak of his cap to the back of his head. "I man was a dangerous youth dem time!", he says. Boy O boy, this guy has got a wicked an'dangerous walk...ya man! He told me he turned up at Raleigh in response to a job advert, and was unsuccessful on two occasions. He believed the job had gone. Oddly enough, 'the advert was still in the paper after several weeks', he said. Mind you, 'Pretty' succeeded the third time round, but this didn't happen until after Nottingham's West Indian community complained to Jamaican Prime Minister, Mr Norman Washington Manley, during his Nottingham visit (11/9/58) which led in turn to the active intervention of the West Indies Federation who sent a 12-man Delegation headed by Hon Dr Carl George Donald la Corbiniere, Minister of Trade and Industry in the Guyanese Government to meet and discuss certain problems with Managing Director/Chairman of the Board of Raleigh Bicycle Industries Mr George H.B. Wilson in July 1959!

Another factor that led to the riot according to Mike and Trevor Phillips in the "Windrush" publication, was the overcrowding of residents envisaged in rows and rows of terraced houses with residents closely knit together in a typical St Ann's slum. Six to nine in any one bedroom would have been no exaggeration at all. One toilet to be shared amongst several. Such toilet would normally be found outside. A familiar venue at the time was the pawn shop. When times were hard, people found it convenient to take their 'Sunday best' suits, their prized pairs of shoes or wrist watches or even the shirts from off their backs to the shop to pawn just so they could get some ready cash-in-hand to do this, that an the other.

The streets were overcrowded and noisy with children making the best of any play space they could find. Whites and Blacks lived side by side. Having said this, the Indians, (also some Pakistanis) had a rather 'special' role to play in all this. Here is what 'Pegie Man' has to say on the theme of racial discrimination in housing:

> "'Nigga; black bastard go home': A so dem a tel we. Monkey, were is yu tail? Wen yu go a de factry fe get jab, dem tek dung de sign. 'Jab gone'. Wen yu go a white peeple fe go look room, dem tel we sey dem no 'av no room. De Indian! We used to rent room from de Indian dem...plenty Indian house fe rent".

When I arrived in Nottingham in September 1962, I was appalled at the level of poverty which existed in the old St Ann's! I use the term 'old St Ann's' to emphasise the fact that a mammoth housing re-organisation took place during the 1970s. This means the whole of the houses in the Robin Hood Chase were demolished and rebuilt. The same went for those houses in and around St Ann's Well Road. Peas Hill Road completely vanished. St Ann's Well Road remains and venues like the Palais de dance, Cavendish Cinema and Lacarno Ballroom still exist although under different names.

Dancing, oddly enough, spells well for the name 'Lacarno'! Today, there are people who still hold that the skills, showmanship and professionalism demonstrated on the dance floor by the West Indian dancers, were in effect, cadinally responsible for inflaming the anger and fury of the Teddy Boys of the 50s. Derby-based Louis Morgan, a 'Nat King Cole'-styled Jamaican balladeer, is one who holds such view. He was based in London, during the time of the Nottingham and Notting Hill riots, and was given to understand that 'Pegie Man' and 'Prettie' were the dancers most fancied by the White girls:

"The Rock'n roll was the 'in thing' in them days ya man! I heard 'Pretty' was a smasher on the dance floor. As for 'Pegie Man', I understand he danced with two girls at a time. They say he used to fling them over his back then do the splits. By the time he managed to turn round, there 'nd then, another two girls would be ready and waiting. Ya man!".

The White girls perhaps relished the fact that Black guys made rock 'n roll look so easy; who to tell, may be they had never ever met such lively guys in all their teeny bops years! The Teddy boys on the other hand saw all this as severe provocation. They were Fascists. A Fascist is one who holds views with respect to Whites being the Master Race. These lads were motivated by the teachings of Oswald Mosley, the leader of the Fascist Political Party in Britain. They wore smart semi-Edwardian black suits with slim neck ties, narrow drainpipe trousers, Parisian black shoes with pointed toes... steel sprigs at the backs of the shoes and hairstyles similar to that of Tony Curtis.

"IMMIGRANTS WERE ASKING WHY SOME MAJOR EMPLOYERS SUCH AS RALEIGH EMPLOYED SO FEW BLACK PEOPLE".

This statement is a quote which was lifted from a Nottingham Evening Post newspaper dated 1 June, 1998. The actual article was designed to draw upon some of the crucial questions West Indians were asking throughout the period of racial disturbances in St Ann's during 1958. The rest of the quote in effect, runs like this:

> "People were saying, 'why are we buying products from these people if they don't employ us? We won't buy your bicycles at all'. That was the first time economic pressure was put upon important companies".

I have found no documented newspaper evidence to justify what West Indians were saying about Raleigh Industries and their employment discriminatory practices during 1958. To be truthful, local newspapers were very very slow to report what these people were saying. Two local newspapers covered the State visit of the West Indies Federation Delegation headed by Jamaican Prime Minister Norman Manley to Nottingham on Thursday 11 September, 1958. I have made detailed studies of reporting undertaken by the Nottingham Guardian Journal and Nottingham Evening Post respectively, and none of them have made any reference to the fears that local West Indians were expressing in relation to prospects of finding work at Raleigh Bicycle Industries.

Prime Minister Manley and the rest of the delegation addressed a Public Meeting at the Colonial Social and Welfare Club on Alfred Street off St Ann's Well Road. The Guardian Journal carried out a comprehensive and detailed report of Manley's main speech during the first part of the meeting. Yet the reporting unfortunately, was not extended to incorporate the final juncture where the people themselves were given a chance to air their concerns about unemployment.

For clarity on what the people were trying to say, let me offer very special thanks to Mr Manley Taylor, a former Trades Union Representative for Raleigh Industries who has kindly agreed to come forward and help me collate some of my information in regards to the employment situation in 1958. By the way, Mr Taylor retired some years ago and currently lives in Jamaica. He was at the crowded Colonial Social and Welfare

41

Club at Alfred St on that eventful night when Prime Minister Manley addressed the people — incidentally, John Wray said:

"There were literally loads of people outside who couldn't get in; For standing room and seating, it was on a 'first-come-first-served' basis. Unfortunately, the place was so packed that I couldn't get in".

In my communications with Mr Taylor, he explained that individual members of the West Indian community, aired their fears of finding work in Nottingham. In the meeting they outlined the fact that Raleigh Industries was refusing to employ Afro-Caribbean people and they demanded to know what the basis of their refusal was. In support of this querry, several invited the theory that Raleigh supplied Rudge and Humber bicycles to over 80 countries and the Caribbean market, at that time, was highly significant!

This meeting generated a wave of questions which only Raleigh Industries could have been able to answer. For instance, Nottingham Evening News dated 11, September 1957 disclosed not just that Raleigh's workforce numbered more than 6,000 but currently had the capacity to attract over 9,000 since the building of its new factory complex which was opened by Field Marshall Montgomery in September 1957. This new 20-acre site extended from Triumph Road all the way down to Orson Drive in Wollaton — so the question people in the meeting were asking was why? Why was Raleigh Industries not drawing some of its work force from the 2,000-strong population of Afro-Caribbeans living in Nottingham?

Mr Manley Taylor was given to understand that it was the Union Officials associated with Raleigh Industries who respectively recommended that the firm's Management uphold a policy of not employing people from the Afro-Caribbean community, since there were fears within the union membership, and the Union Officers wished to understand and interpret the mood of its members correctly.

I recently invited former Nottinghamshire County Councillor Mr George Powe, to comment on Mr Taylor's understanding of the situation, and he informed me that the first time he himself became aware of Raleigh Industries' Union Officers own policy with respect to the full-scale employment of West Indians, was when he paid a visit to invite discussions with Raleigh Management. Mr Glaise and Mr Eddy Gayle accompanied him:

"It wasn't that Raleigh was not employing Black people full-stop. They were employing 'students only'! What Eddy Gayle, Mr Glaise and I were putting to Management (by the way these men are now deceased), is a suggestion to the effect that the firm might like to consider extending their job market not just to students but to the Afro-Caribbean community as a whole. It was at that point that Management told us that they had to think of the interests of Raleigh's Union Officials especially in the light of their recommendations. Nevertheless, they assured us that they would look into the matter. According to the way I read it at the time, it seemed they were just being polite to us... let me add here that our 3-man delegation to Raleigh took place long before the Manley visit".

Prime Minister Manley, according to Mr Manley Taylor, took the opportunity to assure a disgruntled audience that both he and members of the West Indies Federation Delegation are taking the matter very seriously, and will do something about it.

Upon reading a copy of a Raleigh Industries Journal entitled: "Raligram"/Nov 1959 page 12, I gathered that 12 representatives from the West Indies Federation actually paid a visit to the Plant in Nottingham in order to hold talks with the General Manager/and Chairman of the Board of Directors, Mr George H.B. Wilson. Surprisingly, this meeting took place only one year following the Manley visit and the man who led the delegation — the Hon Dr Carl Corbiniere — was in fact, a member of Manley's own team when he visited Nottingham in Sept 1958.

Mr Manley Taylor said he was "ever so surprised" to learn that a load of bicycles which was sent by Raleigh to Jamaica, was in fact shipped back to Raleigh by order of the Jamaican Government on the basis that normal commercial dealings with Raleigh Industries can only be resumed if they undertake to employ members of the Afro-Caribbean community in Nottingham.

What initially struck me about the article from the journal "Raligram", was that no reason was given as to why the West Indies Federation Delegation had come. In fact, on the said page, a group photograph of all 12 delegates was displayed. The Chairman of the Board of Directors for Raleigh was also in the picture. They were all smiling for the camera photo. Oddly enough, no reason was given as to why the delegates decided to pay Raleigh a visit. That reason was kept secret.

Mr Taylor also said he learnt that the Union Officers of Raleigh were approached by Management and advised to change their stance of not hiring West Indian workers. In course of time the policy had changed in a meaningful way so that people from the West Indian sector were beginning to be accepted as employees. Taylor himself was employed at Raleigh in 1969 and went on to become a Union Rep for both Black and White within the present Union membership.

When Mr Taylor joined Raleigh in 1969, there was no Equal Opportunities Policy statement within the clauses of their factory regulations.

The Nottingham and District Community Relations Council which was operative at the time, issued a statement through its Chairman Mr Charan Singh Dhillon to the effect that:

"Employers and Trade Unions in the City, lack any substantial motivation to treat the subject of Equal Opportunity programmes as urgent or even important".

This statement is quoted from a recently published local Report into Race Relations in the City of Nottingham over Forty Years undertaken by the Nottingham and District Racial Equality Council. Page 14 of the said Report quoted a District Secretary of one of the unions at Raleigh during the 60s and 70s as saying that any enquiry into the condition of African Caribbean workers would be in itself counter-productive.

The same page quotes Mr Milton Crosdale, the Director of the Nottingham and District Racial Equality Council, as saying that he had held extensive discussions with a large number of local employers in the past, and the majority, in his view were very reluctant to sign any Declaration with respect to a policy of Equality of Opportunities. Rather, they argued on the basis of their belief that all applicants and employees were treated with equal merit irrespective of their race, colour or ethnicity.

At long last, the 1980s saw 'a wind of change' blowing over the factories, offices, schools and shops in the U.K. as more and more Employers took to incorporating an Equal Opportunities Policy Statement within the framework of their Statute Books. To date, it is fashionable to have a tick-box with Equal Opps Statement affixed at the back of any Application Form. In the meantime, the volume of West Indians finding work at Raleigh Industries has been on the increase ever since. Finally, let us not overlook the role that several activists have played in their bid to bring about change!

WHAT DID JAMAICAN PRIME MINISTER NORMAN WASHINGTON MANLEY SAY TO THE PEOPLE OF NOTTINGHAM?

The Nottingham Evening Post dated Thursday 11 September 1958 put as title of front page story, "WEST INDIANS ARE HERE TO STAY — Manley!". Jamaica, in its own Daily Gleaner dated Friday 12 September 1958 entitled its article, "FUTURE MUST NOT BE BUILT ON FEAR":

> "The future must not be built on fear. Let nobody frighten you. You are here because you have got a right to be here, and you will stay here as long as you want".
>
> © The Gleaner Company Ltd., 12/9/58

The Guardian Journal Friday 12, September quoted him in the event of a Public Meeting at the Colonial Social and Welfare Club on Alfred Street (Nottingham) as saying:

> "West Indians in this country have a right to be here, because they are British subjects, they have a right to stay here as long as they want".

The same paper quoted Manley as outlining three rules the West Indian community could endeavour to put into practice, given the nature of the actual disturbances with which they were faced:

1) "Keep a steady head, and not allow yourselves to be driven to extreme measures.

2) Do not allow anyone to tell you you cannot stay here because you have got civil rights.

3) Build friendship and good feeling; stretch out the hand of friendship to others".

"WEST INDIANS ARE HERE TO STAY"
— Manley

Both Nottingham Guardian Journal and Evening Post portrayed Manley as taking time out not just to shake hands, but listen to what people were saying as he went on his walk-about tour of Alfred Street South, Alfred Street North, St Ann's Well Rd and Robin Hood Chase. Both papers kept "ever so quiet" on all the "hard luck" stories they were sharing with him i.e. this one's window got smashed, that one's house got firebombed, or so and so is finding it ever so difficult to get a job, or this person can't walk late at night because of fear of being attacked by Teddy Boys etc, etc.

On the other hand, what I really appreciated about the Nottingham Guardian's reporting, is the way it took time to emphasise detail which it thought was important. For instance:

"He also went into several houses and sometimes broke away to speak to white people. As he was speaking to one of the white girls he said, 'here is evidence of what they say about Nottingham girls'".

"WENT INTO SEVERAL HOUSES???" come on, said Mr Oscar Reid as I shared this little piece of reporting from the Guardian: "DEM TINGS IS FICTION MAN; HOW CAN A PRIME MINISTER AND HEAD OF A CARIBBEAN DELEGATION FIND TIME FE GO EEN A PEOPLE HOUSE FE GO EAT RICE AN PEAS? I WAS DERE REMEMBER. I SHAKE HAN WID HIM AN I NEVVA SEE HIM GO EEN A NOBADDY HOUSE".

In sticking to my guns, I had to try and memorise the newspaper excerpt word for word:

"As he left the Council House he was mobbed by West Indians wanting to shake his hand. His first call, was at the home of Mr Veron Ringrose, a barber of 133 Alfred Street South, and a prominent worker in the welfare of coloured people. As he left, he affectionately hugged Mrs Ringrose".

Actually, it would be useful to invite Mr or Mrs Ringrose to try and contribute something to this book. I understand they have now moved from Nottingham and I am not quite sure where they are living at this time. Actually, the part that might more invite the possibility of a whistle-stop tour far removed from going into people's houses might look a little more like this:

"Mr Manley was driven following a train of Press and Policemen, to Robin Hood Chase in the City's troubled spot... As he walked up the avenue, Manley was continually stopped by groups of West Indians putting to him their problems and complaints".

"AS HE WALKED UP THE AVENUE" — my, my, this story is embraced in the language-code of a historically celebrated occasion! Most times as I go on the Chase for a morning or late-night walk, I often think of the West Indians of St Ann's who were actually around when Manley arrived on the afternoon of September 11,1958. Again, one of my aims in writing this book is to try and balance the pleasant with the unpleasant. Yes, we are writing about riots, but what can we learn from them? The personal intervention of Norman Washington Manley was about the best thing that could ever have happened!

As a matter of fact, I told myself that somebody would have had to be prepared to document this story so that others could read, understand and relate to it. This is our story. We can't wait for someone else to write it for us. We have got to write it ourselves. We also will have to tell our children that a Barrister-at-Law, named N.W. Manley came to Nottingham to open our eyes so we could understand and appreciate the legal and constitutional implications ascribed to our rights as African Caribbeans especially in a community torn apart by sporadic outbursts of rioting. This was a race riot remember?

And whilst on the subject of race riots did he say anything about race? The Nottingham Guardian Journal would probably have found it very difficult to negate the fact that his visit was not purely about Constitutional Rights but Racial Rights also.

These then are his words as he exclaimed them amidst the rapture of a packed Public Meeting at the Colonial, Social and Welfare Club on Alfred Street in St Ann's:

"In the West Indies, White, Brown and Black live together in peace. No man would dare raise his hand to a White man".

By the time the applause faded out he added:

"The whole of the West Indies was profoundly shocked... English people who say there is no racial prejudice in this country are only fooling themselves".

The Nott'm Journal

Up till this day, nobody seems to be sure of the exact line-up of names comprising the Official Manley Delegation since both newspapers created a muddle of a mix-up as to who was who... the Evening Post named them as:

- Dr Solomons,/Premier of Barbados

- Mr Garnet Gordon,/High Commissioner of Jamaica and

- Dr Carl Lacorbiniere,/Deputy Prime Minister of the West Indies Federation.

The Nottingham Guardian Journal on the other hand identified them as:

- Dr Carl Lacorbiniere,/Deputy Prime Minister of the West Indies Federation

- Dr Patrick Solomon,/Deputy Chief Minister of Trinidad

- Dr H. Cummins,/Prime Minister of Barbados

- Mr Garnet Gordon of the Jamaican High Commision

- Mr Ivo De Souza,/West Indian liason Officer and

- Mr David Muirhead,/West Indian Industrial Relations Officer as well as

- Mrs Edna Manley/wife of the Prime Minister

Dr Solomon could not possibly have been Prime Minister of Barbados and Deputy Chief Minister of Trinidad now which was he?
The Guardian Journal has identified 7 while the Post has only identified 3.

Herewith I Pitman Browne the Author of this book entitled 'CHILDREN GET OUT OF THE GHETTO MENTALITY', shall now take the privilege of inserting 'a small c' by the side of each respective newspaper starting with:

©The Jamaica Daily Gleaner, dated 12/9/58

©The Nottingham Evening Post, dated 11/9/58

©The Nottingham Guardian Journal, dated 12/9/58

©The Nottingham Evening Post, dated 1/6/98

With respect to the relevance of highly important Source Evidence, let me take the opportunity of thanking all three Newspapers for being there when I needed them most. Incidentally, that's what Newspapers are for. They are there to help you if you are researching and are 'hard put' as to where the evidence to back-up your story is going to come from.

RAISING THE PROFILE OF A COMMUNITY COMPRISING AFRO CARIBBEANS AND WHITES.
Mr John Wray, BA., M. Ed, J.P.

When I arrived in the U.K. in September of 1962, the vibes and general repercussions arising from the 1958 State visit of the Manley Delegation provided nothing short of breakfast discussion and convenient table talk. There were stories of Mrs Manley talking to West Indian women and lifting up little babies as she walked through the Robin Hood Chase.

Looking back in retrospect, Mr John Wray had this to say:

"I recall that he visited the street that I lived at the time (i.e. Robin Hood Chase), but I was not there at the particular moment this important event took place...
Personally, I did feel that the 1958 disturbances in Nottingham coupled with the Panel's State visit, 'did' make an increasing number of White members of the host community consider more seriously, the issues surrounding the reality of having a Black presence in their midst".

Before I fade out on this particular part of the book — by the way thank you John — former County Councillor George Powe was saying he joined Manley for dinner at the Black Boy Hotel in Nottingham's City centre when the meeting at Alfred Street was terminated. Mr Powe spoke in glowing terms of a Nigerian Political Activist in Nottingham at the time named Brother Steve Sarabasua. Steve was particularly active throughout the whole course of the Manley State Visit. Years later, he went on to play the leading role in founding two Nottingham-based pressure groups against exploitation namely, S.P.A.D.E. and N.A.C.D. These Organisations do not exist anymore. Steve incidentally, is still a resident in the St Ann's area of Nottingham.

CHILDREN:
THEY
ARE
OUR
FUTURE!

Children are like sponges. They absorb. They see and hear. Since they learn through what they see and hear, the language and mannerisms adduced to street culture make them vulnerable to the actual content of what is being said and done. If the language of the adult world is clean, they will internalise it. If language is hewn out of swear words and curse words, they will internalise it just the same.

If there was a war followed by immediate mass-migration, then the sole legacy of what they would be left to take with them even if suitcases of toys, clothes and books were left behind may be nothing more than the bare impressions of life which are already planted in their minds. Consequently, it is what they see and hear which intrinsically will come to form the bedrock of their own cultural capital.

William Blake, the 19th Century English poet tends to treat children as masterful, responsible adults in his famous 'Songs of Innocence and Experience'.

- In being masterful, does it invite one to respond (jump-up and dance to the music) rather than sit coldly and suppress the potent impact the music is making on ones emotions?

- In being masterful, does it invite one to suffer in silence grin and bare it rather than standing up and issuing a fearless challenge on the basis of what one believes to be right?

- In being masterful does it invite one to exercise the wherewithal to forgive other people for their mistakes?

Children are understanding. They seem to possess the natural capacity to forgive others their wrong. Abraham Maslow, the American theorist in 'Towards the Psychology of Being' (1969) says many adults have lost the innate capacity to be themselves. The system of education makes them passive and obedient; hence, adults are almost frightened to be themselves.

Who will be left to deal with the prejudices the adult world has incurred upon itself?

The children!

Who will be left to take the culture forward once the older ones have died?

The children!

Who will be left to reap the consequences of 'unsafe' decisions which we from the adult world have made?

The children!

Who will be the future decision makers of what constitutes good as opposed to unacceptable (corrupt) behaviour?

The children!

Who will be our future legislators?

The children!

Who will be our future Social Workers?

The children!

Who will be our future teachers?

The children!

Who will be our future undertakers to assist in the burial of those victims lying dead in the streets of Nottingham as a result of affrays between rival gangs from St Ann's and Meadows armed with baseball bats?

The children!

Who will be the future candidates from the Afro-Caribbean community to stand at the next General Election in order to help to ensure adequate Parliamentary representation?

The children!

Who will be the future community leaders to mobilise yet a younger generation into the setting up of self-help groups?

The children!

Who will be the future Police Officers who will go out on the beat in order to take a stand in respect of the maintenance of law and order on the streets of Nottingham?

The children!

Who will be the future vanguards at the forefront of any struggle to do with Police misuse of power?

The children!

Who will be our future High Court Judges?

The children!

Who will be our future Barristers?

The children!

Who will be our future Solicitors?

The children!

Who will be our future Magistrates?

The children!

Who will be our future Customs and Excise Officers at the forefront of the fight against the importation of banned Class A drugs like cocaine and heroin?

The children!

Who will be our future historians?

The children!

Who will be our future anthropologists?

The children!

Who will be the future script writers for soap operas which are yet to be written and presented in a way as to reflect the feelings, hopes and aspirations of our people?

The children!

Who will be the future pop stars who will continue to spread messages that make love look somewhat soft, soppy and sentimental but love just the same?

The children!

Who will be the future political activists to mount full-scale challenges on the bastions of Western monopolist imperialist powers who are still holding African nations to ransom in a way as to reduce their coffee, cocoa, banana, spices, mangoes, pumpkins, pines, oranges and grapefruits to cheap cash crop production levels stipulating practically 'little or nothing' in return?

The children!

What sector of our present population is mostly in need of the basic education enabling us all to learn to read and write?

The children!

What sector of our present population is mostly in need of language and science skills to enhance our innate capacity to negotiate?

The children!

What sector of our present population stands mostly in need of levels of information which have deliberately been kept back years ago purely for the purposes of colonial expansion?

The children!

Which sector of our present population stands most to benefit from the actual truth as to where Greek philosophers <u>Socrates</u>, <u>Plato</u>, <u>Pythagoras</u> and <u>Aristotle</u> got their education from?

The children!

Which sector of our present population will be in a position to make up their minds for themselves once they have been informed that <u>Socrates</u>, <u>Plato</u>, <u>Pythagoras</u> and <u>Aristotle</u> were <u>schooled by the African Professors of the Egyptian Schools of</u> <u>Metaphysical Sciences</u>, and that to become Initiates of such sacred institutions they would have had to accede first of all to the requirements of circumcision and baptism?

The children!

Which sector of our present population have need to understand that Pythagoras did not invent the square of the hypotinuse of a right angled triangle, and that the knowledge in regard to this calculation was included in the grand package of science subjects (Maths, Geometry and Trigonometry) which Pythagoras had to learn from the Educational Masters of the Egyptian Mystery System?

The children!

Which sector of our present population stands most in need of access to the source from whence all this 'new' information comes ("Stolen Legacy" written by George G.M. James in 1957)?

The children!

Which sector of our present population stands most in need of updated information suggesting that Christopher Columbus did not in fact discover Jamaica in 1492 since Arawak Indians were already found to be living there?

The children!

Which sector of our present population stands most in need of updated information suggesting that Christopher Columbus did not discover the New World in terms of Amerigo (re-named America) during the 1400s — such discovery in effect, was undertaken over 400 years earlier by some African explorers from Madagascar?

The children!

Which sector of our present population stands most in need of updated information suggesting that the supposed 'Lake Victoria' in terms of an African discovery attributed to the English explorer Robert Speke later knighted 'Sir' Robert Speke by Queen Victoria, was in the words of former Archbishop of Cape Town Desmond Tutu, "not even a discovery at all", for the simple reason that Africans have been honouring this Great Lake by the name 'Nyanza' for thousands of years, so that for Robert Speke, this was quite rightly not a discovery at all, but just part of his own geographical learning process?

The children!

Which sector of our present population has need to access the information within the context of any geography lesson, that Palestine up till 1885 was still considered (in the words of the Editors Beard and Dillon of the 1884 Family Bible) "part of Black Africa"?

The children!

Which sector of our present population has need to access the actual reason as to why Palestine was no more going to be part of Black Africa, and that the purpose for holding the Berlin Conference attended by leaders of Britain, Belgium, France, Germany, Italy, Spain and the United States in 1885, was to ensure that a new 'Arab Caucasian' identity was introduced so that Palestine (as well as Egypt, Lybia, Saudia Arabia, Iran, Irak, Mauritania, Morocco etc) from now onwards would be looked upon as strictly 'Caucasian'?

The children!

Which sector of our present population has need to know that Bethlehem, the birth place of Jesus Christ, was populated by Black Africans round about 2,000 years ago, and that Christ and his disciples were in fact, Black Africans by race?

The children!

Which sector of our present population needs to appreciate and understand that the name <u>Christ</u> came from the Greek '<u>Christo</u>' which in turn came from the Hindu 'Krishna' meaning 'the Black One', and that '<u>Krishna</u>' (see 'Book of the Beginnings'/1833/Gerald Massey) is an actual transliteration of the word '<u>KRST</u>' from the ancient Egyptian hierogliphics... and that '<u>KRST</u>' was referring to the Christ child Horus who Massey describes as <u>the world's first Black Christ</u>?

The children!

Which sector of our present population has need to know that a population study of ancient Palestine with the help of what could be seen of exhumed bones, fossils and ancient manuscripts, was carried out by Donovan Joyce, an English naturalised American as explained in his classic 1974 book entitled "THE JESUS SCROLL", in which he shared and disclosed to the amazement of the American people that <u>all of the inhabitants of the southern cities of Palestine (i.e. Jericho, Bethlehem, Jerusalem, all along the Judean hills and the shores of the Dead sea) were in fact, populated by Black Africans during the time of Christ</u>?

The children!

What sector of our present population has need to know that "THE JESUS SCROLL" by Donovan Joyce was banned by the American Government because this highly informative book not only disclosed that all the Jewish factions encompassing southern Palestine namely, the Pharisees, Saducees, Scribes, Chief Priests, Publicans and Essenes were housed under the umbrella of the largest and most dominant jewish tribe (i.e. <u>THE TRIBE OF JUDAH</u>)?

The children!

What sector of our present population has need to know that Christ hailed from the TRIBE OF JUDAH and that the Hosmonian dynasty of Black African Priests and Kings which came from out of this tribe, was known by a much more popular name: "THE MACCABBES!" — ruling in Judea from 142B.C to 37B.C.?

The children!

What sector of our present population has need to know that the actual logo of the Hosmonian dynasty was the black panther from whence the American 1960s Black Panther organisation got its name?

The children!

What sector of our present population has need to know that the actual source evidence of Christ's African identity in earlier Greek bibles like Codex Sinaiaticus, Codex Vaticanus, Codex Bobiensis, Codex Syriacus and Codex Alexandrina made reference to "hair like lamb's wool" meaning hair that is 'short, thick and crisp' (see the 1986 New York Random House Dictionary) whereas the1611 King James' Authorised Version reworded it to read "his hairs and his head was white as wool as white as snow" so as to avoid mentioning short, thick and crisp hair of young lambs (nicknamed 'blackhead lambs') as conveniently ascribed to Black people's hair?

The children!

What sector of our present population has need to know and appreciate that "Feet of brass as if burned in a fire" in the verse following from Revelation 1:14, is Black in skin-colour since ancient brass made of copper and tin was actually dark bronze which in effect helps to draw the semblance of a complete picture in respect of a Messiah portrayed with short, thick crisp African hair and Black African feet?

The children!

Which sector of our present population needs to ask whether or not Jesus was a Christian?

The children!

Which sector of the population needs to know that terms like 'Christ'/or 'Christian' were never (I repeat never ever) used by him nor his disciples during the whole of their lives on earth?

The children!

Which sector of our present population needs to understand and appreciate that 'Nazorean' — the Nazoreans were described 'as the maintainers and preservers of the teachings of original Israel' — and this was the actual term applied to Jesus and his followers, so that 'Christian' a pagan (better still, 'nick' name was used by outsiders to describe members of the Early Church in Antioch more than 40 years after the death of Jesus?

The children!

(see Acts 11:26: if Jesus came in this room today he would probably be 'very surprised' to hear us describing him as a Christian... in his birth, death and resurrection he never ever was a Christian. In Emporer Nero's day when they were persecuted, they were called "Essenes", says Ken Clayton in 'Jesus and the Scrolls' 1992.

Which sector of our present population should have free access to this kind of information?

The children!

Which sector of our present population should also have free and unbridled access to the 'new' and current outpouring of Asia-centric Historical writing which suggests that Jesus left Palestine at the tender age of 13 thereby returning at 29 to be baptized by St John, and that all those lost years –of which Matthew, Mark, Luke and John have "remained quiet" — were spent travelling, studying and teaching in Nepal, Tibet and the rest of the Indian sub-continent?

The children!

Which sector of our present population will have need to examine for themselves what our Asian Historians are saying, and start by reading Professor Fida Hassnain's 1992 book entitled "In Search of the Historical Jesus"?

The children!

Which sector of our present population have need to appreciate that the correct name of 'Jesus' in Hebrew is 'YASHUA' — taken from Joshua — meaning 'DELIVERER' and that it was the Greeks who named him 'AESOUS' and Romans 'ISUS', and King James translators 'JESUS'?

The children!

Which sector of our present population have need to appreciate that his correct name is YASHUA BEN JOSEPH? — i.e. son of Joseph?

The children!

Which sector of our present population stands more to benefit from the simple fact that World History is not just about Europeans alone, and in order to effect a more honest and global picture, we will have to recognise that Asian and African Historians were in business long, long, long before the rise of Europe?

The children!

INVENTIONS:
LANGUAGE
AND
DANCE!

WE TEACH, THEY LEARN!

*Mr Colin Mascoll M.A. —
Manager of Team LIBRA,
Nottingham City Council*

Remember the host community has benefited and is still continuing to benefit from the rich and diverse culture we have to offer. For instance, the way we celebrate our birthdays, christenings, deaths, anniversaries etc with each respective design of dress conferring its own distinctive message on the actual nature of the celebration <u>we teach yes? We teach and they learn</u>! As for music good heavens, every piece of music we have ever invented, brings with it, its own dance: At the turn of the 60s Little Richard and the Rock'n Roll followed by Chubby Chekker and the twist, then comes Prince Buster and the Blue Beat, Millie and the Ska, the Mytals with their Rock Steady, Johnny Nash with Lover's Rock, Bob Marley and Reggae, plus Michael Jackson and his Moon Raker Acrobatic Dance, through to the likes of Break Dance where youths literally dance on their heads to the crazy new multi-mix concoction of Ragga and Hip-Hop. <u>We teach yes? We teach and they learn</u>!

The English generally speaking, are rigid in their dance, probably because they have a strange tendency to be mathematical and calculating so when it comes to the art of dancing, it seems to come more from committing certain routines to memory. Given that our Black youths are natural choreographers, we tend to try and avoid routine, preferring instead to venture something that's different. Quite rightly, we are the ones who inspire other cultures to be inventive and creative, <u>we teach yes? We teach, and they learn</u>!

Look at the way one Afro-Caribbean youth signals the attention of another: "Yow"! (rather spontaneous...sounds original if you ask me.)

'Hello' will never ever be the same again. 'The guy played some piano, I tell you the guy is "hard" man! Here the word "hard" is literally transformed to mean 'good'. Just walk along the streets of Harlem U.S.A. and what do you get? 'This "cat" is really "cool" man! "Cat" and "cool" are significant innovations in the development of English Language would you not agree? And speaking of innovations what about the word "bad"? During the 1980s Michael Jackson revolutionised "bad" to mean good maaan, you ain't seen nothin' yet! Wait till you hear words like "wicked" and "dreadful": when you are past clever(???) then that means YOU ARE DREADER THAN DREAD which means <u>we teach yes</u>? <u>We teach and they learn</u>!

From the corridors of the United States throughout the 60s it used to be 'Afro' hair style with Angela Davis and the Jackson 5. And out of the Trench Town Reggae industry Jamaican-style, natty dread was springing-up like nobody's business. All of a sudden John Lennon and Yoko Ono wanted to wear their hair 12 feet long. Then the braids — 'cane row' — which is distinctively African became the fashionable hair style of Bo Derek. People started callin it the 'Bo Derek'! Maan I tell you something: all the other little girls from the other cultures are watching our girls. Rings in the nose and ears are associated with African culture, but are taken on board by some White Youths purely for fashion. All it boils down to is, <u>we teach yes</u>? <u>We teach and they learn</u>!

What about the turning of the peak of the cap to the back of the head? Fashion designers in the business are on the look-out for change and this is exactly what they have copied from the Black youths. Have you noticed the number of White youths who are actually playing loud music in fast cars, now where did they get that from? Right you've guessed it. Incidentally, there are things you can do with jeans, you can turn them into patched denims or denims without any patch so they can see your bare skin. You can cut off the bottoms and shred them... that's called 'shredding' now who did they copy this style from? That's right you have guessed <u>we teach yes</u>? <u>We teach and they learn</u>!

We have not even started talking about food yet. Food, food, food where are you? <u>Egg and chips, sausage and chips, steak and chips, ham and chips, spam and chips, peas and chips, and pie and chips, mushroom and chips</u> come on man, they have overworked the poor old chips!! These people need to diversify their foods. In the Caribbean we have a different dish for each day of the week:

Let's strike-up the Reggae Band with a typical West Indian Friday morning breakfast of bammy, calalloo and salt fish followed by lunch time boiled banana with mackerel and delicious rum punch. Breakfasts and dinners tend to vary depending on which West Indian island you visit. On a Saturday morning, fried dumplings laced with ackee and salt fish is a preference for some, but for others, it will definitely be fried fritters, onions and coconut run-down. When it's time for lunch, various soup dishes are filled from a great big pot of Saturday afternoon beef soup packed with cart-wheel dumplings, yams and sweet potatoes. After such a heavy afternoon meal, most people just go for a light night cap of Ovaltine and a few biscuits just before retiring to bed.

Sunday morning breakfast is graced with fried plantain, boiled eggs and tomato followed by an after-church Sunday lunch of rice and red peas with curried mutton followed by delicious coconut water or ice-cream. On a Sunday night, one can definitely be sure of a buttered slice of hard-dough bread with a mug of home grown West Indian hot chocolate just before going to bed. We are talking about three meals, yes three meals in one day now this is reality. For nutritional value this is ace! This does not even include in-betweens like roast corn, tangerines, guineps, star apples, rose apples, sour sop, nase berries, pine, papaya, passion fruit and mangoes of all variety. Right now, the host community is learning to be diverse in its attitudes to eating. West Indian restaurants provide the most diverse of all the restaurants in this country we teach yes? We teach and they learn!

And moving from one kind of food to another what about peanuts? Yes peanuts. George Washington Carver, a famous African-American Scientist, made over 100 different substances from peanuts, two of which is oil and peanut butter. Moving now to the electrical, let's say with the case of the carbon filament which is responsible for giving us permanent lasting electricity in our bulbs, that Thomas Edison is the name we will all remember! He ended up taking the credit for the successful breakthrough. Yet it was Lewis Howard Latimer, an African American member of his own team who invented this product. This reminds me so much of the scenario involving Florence Nightengale the Nurse who Western Scholarship has accorded full credit for founding and spear-heading the Nursing profession, yet the praises of Mary Seacole, the African Caribbean Nurse/and Doctor from her team who attended all the wounded and dying throughout the course of the war in the Crimea, has in effect remained unmentioned in books and films that document the life of Florence Nightengale now is this fair? Yet the truth in effect, becomes rather like a recurring refrain when it says <u>we teach yes? We teach and they learn</u>!

Unfortunately, our youths have got to make-do with the sort of media images that tend to rubbish everything our foreparents have invented and contributed. For instance, a guy in Africa cuts bamboo and makes a flute. Flutes eventually start finding their way into the symphony orchestras of Europe and who gets the credit? Look at how the Indian smoke signals and the African tom-toms were looked down upon by the Europeans as primitive forms of communication: what were those techniques designed to do, send messages right? Yet they have laid the type of foundation and ground work leading to today's mobile phone <u>we teach yes? We teach, and they learn</u>.

All I am trying to say in principle to our youths in St Ann's, Meadows and Radford is this: as a race, our contribution is far more than we will ever be given credit for! I am not here to put anybody down. The question that stands before us is this: Given that we have a culture of our own, the very culture I have been trying to identify from the outset of these pages, why not try? Why not try and use our culture to the best of our advantage? When I was an 18 year-old back home in Barbados do you know what I used to do? I used to preach yes, preach in church. The church provided the foundation for others like me to learn to love my brother, my sister and my neighbour.
I just used this in terms of an example to say to our young people right now that it is the overall aspect of oneness, respect and community spirit that is missing in our community. To help put this right, we need to foster an attitude of self-respect. This in turn will result in a general respect for our women, respect for our elders, and respect the lives of one another over which we neither have the right to give let alone the right to take. We intend to do the very best we can to eradicate these discrepancies and imbalances from our present society.

LOVE AND RESPECT!
COLIN!

HEAR
THE
VIEWS
OF
OUR
YOUTHS
AS
THEY
TALK
ABOUT MUSIC!

KARIBU HOSTEL YOUTHS:
RAGGA OR REGGAE?

"It's all fashion", says Gary. "Ragga is all fashion; it's all trend; really, it's just like watching bad cowboys on TV. It inspires you to do the same".

Jason:

"I can listen to th' sort of negative images piped out of some CD or other, but it doesn't mean I'm going to be influenced by it does it? Music is music. I make up ma mind wot I want to internalise and so forth..."

As I sat with pencil and notebook amidst the comfortable setting of a sunny Saturday afternoon discussion, I asked them to define the meaning of Ragga:

Clark:

"Ragga is bashment type music with DJ's M C'-ing on the mike in front of a full house. For instance, Beeny Man, and Ninja Man are rap artists who are two of the known names in the business".

Jason:

"You've even got bashment clothes like Moschino-styled baggy trouses £80, Vicace shirt f' nearly £100, Rebok trainers from £60 upwards. Gold teeth and wrist bangles are also part of the fashion — not to speak of the type of cars they drive, like Lexus an' that. To complete everything, some of 'em wear dark glasses... mek dem look cool an nice... cool as ice... see wa a mean? ('smiles')".

Clark:

"The music tends to be very fast, and high-pitched. What we get, is drum and bass just going, going, going...not much vocal".

And now, here is Jahkilah, the only girl in the discussion so far:

"This is it you see. Ragga is not like beautiful songs. The sound is too harsh. Reggae is more beautiful. Reggae is more softer... like chill-out music. With Beeny Man and Ninja Man you are not talking bout good lyrics at all; them is certainly not the type a lyrics a girl would sit down and listen to. For a start, them lyrics are embarrassing; they go on an on... sometimes they're a bit much."

This is a fair comment to make. Jason answers the criticism:

"I don't say any of it is bad. In effect, what might be sounding harsh to you, is genuine experience f' them. Look at the gun culture for instance. For us, it takes nothing to shoot bow, bow, bow at the start of a CD down at the club on the night; these DJ's on the other hand, are actually reporting the gun culture as real as it is to them. In fact they don't write songs. If they are bringing the true culture of oppression and gun violence on the street, then yes, it will sound harsh at times".

Clark:

Check de lyrics! Dem lyrics is real. Dis is not a fabrication. Dis is de ghetto. For a start, dem don't lie. Dem tell it like it is. Rap artist don't' write songs. Dem stand up an' tel de story bout poverty an oppression an hard life een a de ghetto... dat is fa real!"

Mind you, while these two views were being expressed, I felt like picking up on what Vanessa, the St Ann's Sister of the Order of Rastafari was saying to me some weeks ago about Ragga:

"Ragga is a hybrid multi-mix concoction of Reggae and Pop. They call it Acid music or Garage music. You've got to drop an E to understand it. It's high-pitched all the way through and doesn't make any sense. If you want to recapture that wonderful feeling of body and soul, you've got to go back to Reggae. It takes a Reggae artist to convey the message. Take Erica Badoo and Lauren Hill for instance: they don't wear false eyelashes or contact lens; they don't even bother to show a leg. Erica is letting you know that Egypt is Kemet. In her kind of lyrics, she is letting you know that a girl's menstrual cycle moves 365 degrees with the moon — in other words, there is always something educational!

This could never be Ragga. Ragga is hype. Ragga causes havoc. Ragga encourage the kids to be zombies and blockheads. The promoters want to promote slackness..."

While this was going through my mind, Youth Man Roydel walked in:

"Dis Ninja Man, an Beeny Man... dem tings is slackniss wey dem a kyp up! I find dat one by one dem a start fe change now. Look pan Shabba Ranks? Im a try fe talk some good lyrics an ting; Im a change-up! Slackniss fe mek money? Dem tings finish! Yellow Man finish!!"

As the discussion opens-up, we start to draw something from out of the all-night rave. A kind of connection between <u>Ragga, Dance</u> and <u>Rave</u> is envisaged as Jason steps in:

"When you go to a rave what is it that keeps the kids going all night? Speed yes speed and ecstasy! These drugs came out on the market, at a time when <u>Ragga</u> and <u>Dance</u> and <u>Rave</u> were spreading like wild fire".

James contributed to the discussion by stressing that Garage music was O.K. in its correct context providing there was a market for it, but there came a time when he would much have prefered to wind down and relax to a Reggae number by Bob Marley. And speaking of Reggae, I took the opportunity of asking anyone who wished to give me a definition of Reggae. At that juncture, we were greatly helped by Leslie Robinson:

"No matter where you go, the only 'real' music there is, is reggae. Reggae is 'real' in the sense that it gives you history. It gives you education. It gives you enlightenment. It tells you what is happening in the world. Reggae acts like media doesn't it? During the 60s, many of the Reggae records told you what was happening in the gun Courts of Jamaica... which rude boy got locked-up and who got bailed. Any Judge presiding in a guncourt would be nicknamed Judge Dread. Artists like Berris Hammond, Freddy Mc Greggor, Dennis Brown, Peter Tosh, Bunny Wailer and Bob Marley will never die. You only need to go on the Continent to feel the impact of these men on the music market!"

Youth Man Roydel:

"Wid musicians like Sisla, de music business wil nevva die why? Because dis man have a message. Him a cum wid sum real consciousness; peeple dem a look... dem a look fe spiritual liberation. Musician like Sisla, come fe clean up de industry an mek betta citizens af dis community".

There and then, I took the opportunity of asking why was it that Bob Marley's success was so phenomenal". Clark stepped in:

"Yu se: For a start he wasn't singing bout oppression all de time. What made Marley special, was de fact that him did a show us a way forward. For instance, one a de time, he was speakin bout political unity between de Manley and Seaga political factions. Yu rememba sey im did invite de two leader dem pan de stage fe hold hands? All dem ting is good" 'Let's get together an it'll be all right... a soh de song go".

Far from all of this wonderful ('let's get together') rhetoric, there surely is something which is eating away at the very roots of our economic survival as African Caribbeans! To be truthful, I am very pleased that Leslie Robinson chose to focus on it:

"When these youths dress themselves in, £100 Moschino shirt, £90 Moschino trousers, £100 Nike trainers ('bashment' dis and 'bashment' dat), they are literally robbing their one another to help support big Capitalists who are helping to further Western interests".

This sounds pretty much like what our man Leslie Davis has been saying. In fact, he puts it even stronger:

"A youth buying a pair of Nike trainers for £85 might live in a Council house — he and his Mom. Right there he is making a big sacrifice. The truth is, he might be unemployed. He can't afford it. Yet he is willing to mimic his friend's life-style at any price.
When you hear on the shout, Nike is exploiting thousands of workers by treating them as cheap labour. Between 1997 and 1998 the amount of money Nike and GAP were paying rubber and shoe workers in Vietnam and Korea, fell well below the minimum wage

set by the United Nations. At the end of the day, those people were literally the ones supporting the big Capitalists! A youth more often than not, is not really interested in the power politics behind a pair of trainers is he?"

From the point of view of a general discussion situation, I am confident that these strands of thought will in the end count for something. The youths at Karibu have opened-up very nicely indeed. With this kind of co-operation, at least one reader will stand to benefit from such convivial and wholehearted input.

"CERTAIN TYPES OF MUSIC IS BANNED IN THIS CLUB!"

*Mr Karl White
Leader of the Meadows
Youth and Community
Centre*

"Types of recorded lyrics which are expressly designed to degrade and debase women, are definitely not allowed to be heard within the confines of this building! On the musical front, there is a clear ban", says the Leader of the Meadows Youth and Community Centre Mr Karl White. "How can I be encouraging young men to equate their young women with "bitches" in public yet idolising and adoring them in private? If I did that, then we would all be pandering to double standards: that certainly isn't on. On the subject of race, there are certain CDs which tend to articulate the word "nigger", yet when youths all get together on the football ground, should an opponent decide to call the other a "nigger", it is immediately taken as an offence.

I was told a fight developed at school, and that it started when a White guy called a Black guy "nigger". The teacher stepped in and made it clear he/she would not stand for any such racist remark in school. The parent of the White lad said he/she didn't see a problem at all, since the Black guy had shown no such distaste when he regularly visited her son's house to play CDs explicitly incorporating the use of the word, so that the Black guy relating to "nigger" as prompted by the CD, had never actually treated the word as an offence — he only saw it as entertainment. The point I am trying to make here is that the demonstration of such appalling double standards must now be placed fairly and squarely at the door of the Record Companies. It is all very well for them to market images purely for the purposes of making money, but they need to stop and reflect on questions like who? Who is this appalling lack of respect likely to affect in the end? Just who — who are they trying to destroy? Unfortunately, with entertainment there is a price to pay.

Believe me, it gets worse... in fact, I heard not long ago that a youth was called "nigger", and the matter was taken to court. The plaintiff got off scot free after explaining to the court that he expressed the word "nigger" purely in entertainment terms since it came from the CD's and was associated purely with entertainment, so that within the language of the clubs responsible for targeting youths, such word would by no means be considered revolting or offensive!

My question is now directed to the musicians themselves: What is yesterday's 'Yellow Man' doing about his slack lyrics? What is today's Shabba Ranks doing about sexually explicit terms that cheapen, belittle, demoralise and debase the image of our women? Not very much I suppose. The bottom line is, once they have made their 'blood' money, they tend to seek for greener pastures in the more affluent residential sectors — end of story — so that the actual communities responsible for supporting them will have still remained dilapidated, deteriorated and run down".

THE CREATION OF THE GANGSTER RAP

"Shooting and swear words continue to be part and parcel of the whole bevy of gangster rap images, continues Mr Karl White. "There are clubs in Nottingham which continue to make youths feel comfortable as they walk in with all sorts of swear words from the 'Tupac', 'Puff Daddy' 'Beeny Man', Shabba Ranks and Buji Banton 'bad boy' images. Some come with tattoos emblazoned on their arms, gold chains, gold teeth and gold bracelets".

The word 'bad' is fashionable. To be 'bad' makes one feel real big eh? 'Bad Boy' is a derivative of the 'Rude Boy' image encapsulating the raz-ma-taz of gun shots fired at random with people getting killed or wounded... all simultaneously accompanied by a sitting of 'special' Gun Courts which the Manley Government initiated in Kingston Jamaica during the turbulence and momentum of the Manley/Seaga political election campaigns of the 1970s. To be a 'bad' guy is to develop the capacity to blast each other to smithereens... kingdom come... and let so-and-so know who is boss O.K.? To behave in this shameless, ruthless and lawless manner, one will first of all create one's own turf or territory from where one and one's cronies operate. On the Jamaican horizon, it was the Rude Boys of East Kingston versus the Rude Boys of West Kingston.

On the Nottingham home front this is very much the same kind of pattern exhibited amongst those youths who feel that St Ann's is their turf, as opposed to the other set who feel that the Meadows is their own home patch.

Having said this, out of bad, comes forth good. If one harks back to the Jamaican situation, one will find that Reggae Star Bob Marley came from out of the Trench Town West Kingston ghetto, with a message of peace and reconciliation. He did this by inviting Prime Minister Michael Manley and Opposition Leader Edward Seaga to join forces with him on the platform. The object of the exercise, was to get both politicians to hold hands thereby reaffirming solidarity and oneness amongst all the divisive factions.

Kwame, the Nottingham Sunday afternoon Radio Broadcaster cites the galaxy of Hip-Hop Ragga videos which are expressly designed to evoke and promote a glamorous life style. A life of fast cars and loud music is what our youths like to copy and emulate. This desire is so deeply entrenched in them that they will stop at nothing to possess the likes of jewellery, designer clothes, shoes by Gooche, not to mention mobile phones. And speaking of mobile phones I am staggered... absolutely flabbergasted when I stop to measure the volume of youths, single mothers and unemployed folks who proudly display mobile phones in their pockets as they walk through the shopping centre arcades.

Mobile phone? Company car? Forget it! When I say the mobile phone is no longer equated with the rich man and his paradise you've got only to look around you to observe the mass influx of mobile phones for yourself. According to a Nottingham Evening Post article dated 1/21/2000, more than six million of them, are currently being used by school children in the Nottinghamshire area. Altogether, there are now 24 million mobile phones in use in the United Kingdom, so much so that Mr Tony Wells, Head of Farnborough School, Clifton, is worried that these giant manufacturers have turned to exploiting the school children mass market purely for financial gain. — By the way, I too must try and 'get in the groove'... get myself a mobile why not... spoil myself... go on... ('smiles')?

Touching once again on the whole subject of truancy, Kwame feels there are links between truancy and expulsion. .i.e. truancy automatically creates conditions for school expulsions:

"Social exclusion includes the racist policy of expelling Black youths from school at an alarming rate, in so much that they will have very little, or no prospects whatsoever of finding employment; hence, they are likely to resort to other methods of gratification such as craving the glamorous life-styles exhibited in these Hip-Hop Ragga videos. These images allow false hopes and false consciousness to thrive and flourish. Through false hopes, drugs become the number one money earner so that once the Police gets involved, youths tread a thin fine line between the prospects of a criminal record punctuated by imprisonment, coupled with the traumas, emotional heartbreaks and sleepless nights experienced by their parents and loved ones".

Mr Karl White finally warns against a major temptation faced by our youths... the temptation to get rich too quickly; with drugs, unfortunately there is a price to pay and that is sad!

CHILDREN
PLAYING
TRUANT
FROM
SCHOOL

LOOKING AT TRUANCY IN THE MEADOWS
— the 'At Risk' Project
(Snippets from a chat with some 14 to 16 year-old youths)

" I don't like school" said 15-year-old Rikki.

"Why? Why don't you like school Rikki?"

"I just don't like school full stop".

"Don't you like any of the subjects on the curriculum?"

"No; I skive lessons".

"Days at a time?"

"No; just the odd lesson or so".

"You skive on your own do you?"

"No; me and m'friend".

"Do you like going to the 'At Risk' Project at the Meadows Youth and Community Centre on a Friday morning?"

"Yes".

"More than school?"

"yes".

"Why?"

"They don't bore you with Maths 'nd English an' that".

"What do you like about the 'At Risk' Project?"

"They teach me social skills".

Social skills, according to Paula Yellop, one of the Youth Workers involved in the 'At Risk' Project, may take the form of issue based projects like:

- Watching a video on race followed by a discussion, or

- Accompanying the youths to the Nottingham Forest Ground at City Ground to get acquainted with computer skills,

- Taking them to the Galleries of Justice and the Crown Court, so they can understand not just the penalty as received by the defendant, but the personal distress that is brought on the whole family, or

- Playing a game of Pool. ('Playing pool', said Paula, is not necessarily about potting a ball for the sake of it; Their concentration span in a given study situation, is probably not more than between 3 to 5 minutes. If they play pool, we hope it will encourage group participation, aid concentration and instil more co-ordination and interaction amongst the group).

From a one-to-one discussion with Allan (12) and Adrian (14), it occurred to me that being expelled from school was certainly not as disastrous as it may sound, since it helped in some way to make truancy easier: both incidentally, had been expelled on a number of occasions for fighting. Adrian said rather casually:

" I have been expelled 3 times; I'm not bothered".
" In 9th year I used to skive a lot", said Carl.

What struck me most of all, was that nobody seemed to like anything their own school had to offer. For instance, Adam would like to acquire the skill of repairing bikes, Rikki hopes to be a D.J., Alan wishes to be a mechanic, Tremayne wants to be a footballer and Adrian would like to go into the carpenter and joinery trade. Carl seemed unclear as to what he might like to do. On a whole it is rather sad to see so little faith displayed in the school system. School to these youths seems nothing more than gossip or a laugh, if not plain boring!

Mr Karl White, the Leader in charge of the Meadows Youth and Community Centre, linked one of the underlying causes of this boredom to a lack of parenting skills:

"One morning, I met a 15-year-old girl on her way to school, so I asked her why it was that she was so late — by the way, her name used to be on the register of our 'At Risk' project. She said she woke up but went back to bed. Got up to go to school late because she knew her dad would be coming back to check if she had gone. She said she liked it better when her Mom was there. When I asked her why, she explained that her Mom encouraged her to get up early, get dressed and wait till Dad was gone. No sooner than Dad was gone, she was allowed to get back into bed and stay at home".

With such low levels of self-esteem coming from a mother what else can one expect of a 15-year-old daughter? The world is competitive enough as it is. Those who are over-qualified still can't get jobs. Given that girls are growing up so much faster than boys, my gosh what sort of future is she hoping to have if a mother is actively encouraging her own daughter to sleep it off? This puts me in mind of a similar story as told this time by Mr Colin Mascoll, the Manager of Team LIBRA, the Radford youth Project. A Nottingham 14-year-old after returning from a Jamaican holiday, boasted of the wonderful times experienced whilst enjoining father, mother and other family members on the verandah smoking ganja. No moral correctness! No discipline! This begs the question: Will these same parents be now encouraging their 14-year-old to sell ganja to get money to buy Rebok trainers for £90 and Moschino trousers for £100? When times get harder and harder, will the truant of a 15-year-old be sent by her mother to make money in and around the back streets of Forest Road? To pinpoint one of the underlying causes of truancy, it will have to be acknowledged that parenting skills are in some cases, the main underlying cause.

With a note of somewhat sombre reflection, Mr Karl White the Leader in charge of the Meadows Youth and Community Centre says:

"The parent in some cases does not even encourage the child to put his/her own clothes in the washing machine, or make-up his/her own bed, so as to allow self-pride and initiative to develop. Consequently, by the time he/she gets to school and starts displaying such woeful lack of drive, initiative and motivation, it is beginning to look as though the fault rests only with the child. I have had to go into homes of children according to my line of work and what strikes me from some of the parents, is the language they use. Expletives and four-letter words come like nothing in front of their children.

'Bend the tree', an old proverb, 'when it is young'. How under God's heaven are they going to expect to dance abroad if they haven't even learned how to dance at home? As opposed to my own upbringing in the West Indies we were pro-Police, whereas these children are inclined to be anti-Police, anti-correction with respect to their own parents so that by the time they get to school, they find it difficult to appreciate the correctness that teachers instil... such correctness just seems to run-off like water on a duck's back why? Because some of the vital parenting skills are lacking. Unlike the old days when the whole family used to sit around the telly, we find mothers nowadays literally locking their children away in some TV video games room where they will now be exposed to the so-called 'wonderful' world of glamorised violence... jumping over high walls, chopping-off necks and registering quick kicks to the head, quick, quick, quick like a flash! With mothers leading lives which are now independent of their children, there is a tendency for them to want to go dancing, or go to some pub or club. Consequently, the video games pastime if anything, will have to be considered the number one influence in the eyes of these young ones".

SKULLING THE DAY FROM SCHOOL:
Pitman Browne

Two yung gal
Nothing to do
No no no
Nothing to do
Up and down demma
Up an down demma
Idle!
Idle!
All de time me sey
Idle!
Idle!
NOTHING TO DO!

Nothing to do but walk de street
Walk which street?
Blue Bell Hill uppa
Blue Bell Hill... ...
Any old time
Day or night
Tek it or leave it
Life's not right
Blue Bell Hill is
Here to stay... ...
Dis is life... ...
IN ST ANN'S.

Morning noon
All in tune
Throughtout de evening and da night
Why no school
Not a school
Not a thing for
Dem to do.
Wy demma play
Play de fool
Wastin' time

Hyde fr'm school
ALL DE TIME DEMMA HIDE AN HIDE

Hide from school demma
Kick de can demma
Play football demma
Laugh an joke demma
Walk an talk demma
Play hop skotch demma
Shout an sing demma
Waste dem time demma
Chant an chant demma
Dress look nice demma
Eat good food demma
Kick de dog demma
PLAY DE FOOL!

        Tel me de name a de
        Two yung gal me sey
        Tel me de name a de
        Two yung gal... ...
        One name Tara
        Once name Dawn
        Dis is nat dem
        Real real name... ...
        Change!
        Change!
        All de time... ...
        NAME OR A NAME IS
        JUS A GAME

How bout school?
Wat bout school
Education!
Education!
Not a school at all in sight... ...
Tel me dis
Wy is dis
Dem suspend
Dem suspend
WHO'S TO BLAME?

Both a dem... ...
Two a dem... ...
One is tall an
One is short
Dem no fear?
Dem no care?
Manvers-Pierrepont!
Manvers-Pierrepont!
Fight w'de school
Fighe f'e yu right
Gal dem/no want... ...
Want no war
Dem no want no war widdi school so
PLAY IT DOWN... ...
PLAY IT COOL... ...

        Tekit to de street and out you go
        Out a de school... ...
        No complain and no big fuss
        Out a de home... ...
        NO MORE RULE!!!
        NO MORE SCHOOL!!!

Tek it to de water
Tek to de wayside
Tek it to de walk and
Tek it to the park and
Tek it to de street and
Tek it to de Vic and
Tek it to de Broad Marsh
Tek it to the trent and
Trent Embankment
Tekit to de green:
HYSON GREEN!!!

        Walk an' talk... ...
        Talk an' walk... ...
        Two pretty gal demma
        Walk an talk... ...
        Tired a de rule

Tired a de homework
Tired a de school and
Tired a de food and
Tired a de beetroot
Tired a de soup and
Tired a de teacher
Tired a de parents
Tired a de cuss cuss
Tired a de put down
Tired a de noise and
Tired a de story
Tired a de vibes anna
PURE BAD VIBES!!!

Big yung bwoy
Likkle yung bwoy
Big big man demma watch dem gal
Watch dem gal demma watch dem gal
Fun f'de run and run f'de fun
Ha! Ha! Ha! Ha! Ha! Ha! Ha! Ha!
Meet de man dem
Meet de boyz dem
Day by day... ...
Sound de horn... ...
LATE AT NIGHT TO DE BIG BOSS HOUSE!!!

Give dem food
Give dem shandy
Give dem brandy
Mek dem randy
Shine and dandy
Take a whiff... ...
Take a spliff... ...
Marijuana!
This won't harm her
Marijuana!
This won't harm her
Marijuana!
YES IT WILL!!!

Who? Who?
Who a de parents
What? What? Wat kinda parents
Leave dem daughter
Absent!
Absent!
Down in de basement
Boyz?
Men??
All nite party
Gambling
Den a de
All nite party Hyson Green at de all-nite party???

THE STORY CONTINUES
TO UNFOLD WHEN:

One of the mothers of the two young girls switches the bedside radio on at her Council-rented Blue Bell Hill terraced house just in time to hear the 8 o'clock morning news coming through from Radio Trent to the tune of :

"The Bamba-Wamba Club at Nottingham's Hyson Green has been the subject of a massive drugs raid by an undercover Police operation code-named "HURRICANE HURRY-UP COME DOWN" during the early hours of 2.00a.m. this morning. Cannabis to the estimated market value of £3000,000 was seized as well as porno video cassettes containing 'hard-core' sexually explicit material. The so-called 'President' (president — mash-up-de-resident) Mr S.J. Mitchmad Timson affectionately known as 'Bagga-Wagga' is still at large.

So far, six men are being arrested for drugs-related offences while two women (Ruby Rass and her friend Pissin Lizzie) are being cautioned at the Radford Road Police Station for being drunken and disorderly.

And finally, just to end, two young girls giving their names as Tara and Dawn, were also held in the drugs-related raid, and are at present helping Police with their enquiries".

Later that day, both mothers — one obviously very distraught — turned up at the Police Station to give moral support to their daughters. These two girls were cautioned and released. The fact that they had never been in trouble with the Police before, went in their favour. Both of them are aged 15. In other words, they are in the prime of their youth and in the eyes of the law, are 'minors' since they are under the age of 16. Going to borstal, could be seen as the 'worst' family tragedy from the point of view of parents no matter how bad the nature of existing relations between them and their children. In society, the thought of a borstal carries with it such a stigma! When one completes one's term of confinement in a borstal, it is rendered incumbent upon him/her to be as truthful and honest as possible when filling-out a job application form. All such information is recorded and held for future reference in the Police computerised data system. If one answers on the application form "no, I have never

85

been in trouble with the Police before", then one is setting one's self at the risk of being found out. If one then, is found to be lying, then it automatically makes matters worse.

In the long run, it would be best to avoid these repercussions by not going into a borstal in the first place. Correction at home is stigma-less. Correction at school has advantages in the sense that we are there for one purpose only — that is to learn!

All the characters in this story are fictitious. They are not real. Having said that, I have a view to the effect that expulsions were in progress at Manvers-Pierrepont during the times when I used to live at Blue Bell Hill Road. By the way, Manvers, closed over 12 years ago. On the occasion of one such expulsion, I felt impelled to knock on doors in order to issue leaflet invitations to parents who might wish to come along to a special Schools Expulsions seminar which was to be convened at the Ukaidi Centre, Marple Square near Woodborough Road. What surprised me, was that most of the parents I spoke to were just not keen on attending this seminar. One parent whose young girl was actually kicking the can in the streets following an expulsion, did not even bother to go along to the Staff at Manvers to sort out the problem involving her daughter's expulsion.

Manvers was conveniently poised as a catchment area for absorbing the volume of students living in and around Blue Bell Hill Road. Unfortuately, it was one of the schools earmarked for closure.

This was very bad news. Many students and parents — some of whom were past students protested. This nonetheless, was not to be. They lost the battle. Manvers was closed. Ukaidi Centre as a matter of coincidence, was also closed.

Hence, My Message To The Girls

TRY AND RESTORE YOUR SELF-ESTEEM!

Brighten up! Lighten up!
Brighten up! Lighten up!
Try and get!
Try and get! Me sey
Try and get — back de
Self-esteem

Look into y're life and
Look f'r y'r right and
Look into y're life and
Look f'r your right... ...
Try and get!
Try and get! Me sey
Try and get — back de
Self-esteem

Beautiful!
Inside outside
Inside outside
Seek!
Seek!
Seek f'r de rest
Bring out de best
Put-it-to-de-test
Try again!

Education
Try again
Education
Never let it rest
Education
Bring out de best
Put-it-to-de test an
Never let it rest

Brighten up! Lighten up
Brighten up! Lighten up!
Try and get!
Try and get! Me sey
Try and get — back de
Self-esteem

Every ting!
Be o'right
Every ting will
Be o'right
Tek it from de root and a
Way to de top
Tek it from de root and a
Way to de top and
Every ting will be o'right.

(Keep repeating this final block of 9 lines until the whole thing fades out).

More Messages To The Girls

GIRLS: GO BACK TO YOUR EDUCATION!!!

These words in effect emerged as a resolution, following a meeting between the two mothers, their daughters and certain members of staff at Manvers-Pierrepont Comprehensive school in St Ann's. Dawn and Tara (incidentally, their 'real' names are Joy Swift and Beverley Needham) were both present at a private Parent-Teachers meeting in order to discuss ways forward especially in the wake of a 3-week expulsion order which was served on them. The girls stenuously denied the actual reason given for the expulsion, and went on to point out that there were other factors involved. They are now saying that they were unfairly treated.

What seemed so bizarre about the whole situation, was the fact that none of the two parents showed-up at the school when their daughters came home with expulsion orders. I find this absolutely incredible! The only factor that served to ignite their wrath and indignation — hence immmediate involvement — was when their daughters landed in trouble with the Police.

O good heavens, I am not saying that all parents are like this. All I am purporting to point out is that there are parents who correct and chastise 'severely' — sometimes all too 'severely' in the interest of their own children. Again, there are parents whose sole intetion is to leave the bulk of the tutorial responsibility to the teacher.

Finally, it is clear that the girls were fed-up with both their teachers and parents:

"Tired a de rule
Tired a de homework
Tired a de school and
Tired a de food and
Tired a de beetroot
Tired a de soup and
Tired a de teacher
Tired a de parents" etc, etc.

POSSIBLE SOLUTIONS TO TRUANCY

I spoke to Merrecher Liburd, Co-ordinator of the Drug Prevention Initiative based at the Meadows, and she identified truancy as one of the possible outcomes attributed to the shortcomings of curriculum organisers. What if the lessons were re-packaged on the basis of individual needs — hence, study groups arising out of these needs?

"You've got to give it to the youths. If they say it's boring, then it's boring! In my capacity as Co-ordinator of the Meadows Drug Prevention Initiative, I am having to interact with 13 to 16-year-olds all the time especially in course of specialist drugs-related workshops, and if I ask them how's school generally and they say it's boring, then I have to believe what they are saying. Needless beating round the bush if the Curriculum Organisers are found woefully lacking in vision and insight. Organisers first of all, need to target the correct age group with the correct work. Once they've got the correct age group, they will now need the correct study methods to attract them.".

In looking back some 15 years ago in my own life, I am having to relate to what Merrecher is saying, just to give an example: This Afro-Caribbean guy was in the A/level Literature class with me. 'Why so much Jane Austen, he kept asking . Why so much Shakespeare? Why 300 years ago? Why not today? What about today's multi-racial society? Nine books and no African-Caribbean authors? No sex? No music? No street culture? With that saying, he went straight out of the class and never came back because the whole thing was just a bore. If a 22-year-old man on a part-time course can be so bored, just imagine what it must be like for a 14-year-old who literally has nowhere else to go but school? More like full-time boredom if you ask me!

Just to draw upon yet a further example of what she is saying, I have tried more than once to enrol on a sound-recording and sound-mixing course at the Confetti Studios here in Nottingham and could I get a space? No! Too late. The place was packed-out with 17 to 19-year-olds; dem pack de place so till it rammed! Here is a good example of study skills targeted to 'correct' age groups!

Merrecher Liburd advises that teachers should ask the children... yes, ask them what they want! Even if it means adapting a whole lesson to music, do it. Frankly, the method in certain situations, might even prove all the more beneficial in the end — rather like 'killing two birds with one stone'! If Curriculum Organisers want the content to reach these children, they will have to start thinking about the methods they are using. Personally, if I could have put all my o/levels or GCSE's to music, I guarantee you I would pass every one of them with a Grade 'A' why? Because Art is creative, and learning is an individual thing.

Just look at the caption on a wall that reads 'THIS BUILDING IS CLOSED': some students might see it flatly as written; others might see and appreciate the 'love and understanding' factor behind the caption, because some have got more imagination than others. As human beings, our personal insights and feelings are displayed on different levels hence, any Curriculum Course Organiser would well be advised that learning is an individual thing. Admittedly, the learning process can become boring and stiff for young people if the course is overwhelmed with academic course requirements.

The academic is just one approach to education. Consider how much more interesting it would be if a 13-year-old was faced with a broad range of educational options! Take the field of life-skills for instance: Family parenting is an excellent life skill to have! So is Drugs re-education. Is there something to be learned about ganja and its use/or misuse? What about street education? What kinds of social skills do we need to deal with street beggars, street musicians, street preachers, drug peddlers and runaways? These skills are transferable. That means, you can take one skill, and apply it to several other situations.

In the school system for instance, how many teachers have decided to spend a whole hour let alone a whole afternoon teaching some of the skills involved in form-filling? What can be more frustrating to a school leaver, than the prospects of failure to find a job or receive placement in Higher education purely because the questions on the form have not been answered properly?

When a student goes out in the 'real' world with the likes of academic A/levels like Politics, Economics and Literature, he or she more often than not, will feel inadequate when faced with community-based problems. What Miss Liburd is intimating for instance, is the plight of the candidate who has done everything right in the Final exam at the Teacher's Training College, yet when faced with a class of children drawn from various backgrounds, such a candidate is already beginning to feel inadequate and out of touch. Whose fault is that? One can't just blame the candidate for being totally unprepared for dealing with a certain type of student (i.e. the 'problem student') — the College responsible for training the candidate must/and should accept some responsibility for the teacher-training technique it currently has on offer!

Another skill which is much in demand once a teenager leaves school, is how best to make the most of a job interview by presenting positive images followed by positive body language. How does one sell one's self? These are life skills worth learning. Passing school exams are useless if you lack the capacity to influence others and assure them that you are the right person for the job!

"Unfortunately", continues Miss Liburd, "there are discrepancies in the system which make life as frustrating as possible for the child who feels passionately convinced that he/or she perhaps might like to pursue voluntary work as a meaningful objective in life. Take a V.S.O. — Voluntary Service Order — qualification for example. This is an internationally recognised qualification which from 21 onwards, if granted, the applicant can be accorded the right to travel to any underdeveloped country and help others in a voluntary capacity.

I applied and was told I wasn't academically qualified to do voluntary work. They were looking for someone who was the recent holder of a degree from a University, now that certainly was not my understanding at all. My greatest attributes to date, are my community development experience. They none the less, didn't quite see it that way.

HOW TO ACCESS FINANCIAL INCENTIVES EMERGING FROM SITUATIONS TO DO WITH EXPULSION AND TRUANCY

Merrecher Liburd is advising Academic Organisations to think more carefully about the pupils rather than the money the pupils attract. For instance, if a child gets expelled or is rendered truant from school, the money for that child's education should be easily accessed so as to allow alternative educational arrangements to be made for that child. Such funding, if released, could assist in employing the services of a Private Tutor, coupled with the provisions for the necessary books. Incidentally, there are parents who for instance, have undertaken to teach their own children for whatever reason.

The potential problem unfortunately both for both parents and alternative agencies, is that this money more often than not, is very hard and difficult to access. The information I am having from a certain place I used to work, is that this money could take as long as three months to access, by which time the school term has either ended, or the matter over the slow passage of time becoming altogether untenable".

To draw conclusions to this article on truancy and your child, I would invite parents to go to any W. H. Smith's shop, and ask for a copy of The National Curriculum Information regarding the educational subjects taught. This will only enhance your child's learning.

GANG
WAR
DOCUMENT

PHASE
TWO

DRUGS! MONEY!!
BLACKMAIL!!! BULLYING!!!!

Gang war gets to the stage where gangsters from Coventry are actually streaming into Nottingham to kidnap their own brothers for the sake of crack-cocaine. A Nottingham drug dealer was recently kidnapped by a Coventry posse. All this led to a Police raid on the home of this man's innocent family. Such family had to endure the traumas of fear, anguish, pain, embarrassment and sleepless nights — is this fair?

Is this what you call brotherly love if your own Black brothers are going to stitch you up just for the sake of crack-cocaine which is going to lead to eventual death? Why are we killing-off our own family? Drugs have turned people into such zombies they can't even think straight. O.K., O.K. — let's be rational:

If a brother should come to my home with a glass of wine, I would be sceptical to drink from the same glass. Yet (!) with a gang, I would not even think twice to smear my lips with another person's ganja butt. This is the only time you see unity... when our Black brothers are actually passing the ganja around from hand to hand.

Organised gangs lead to gang wars. Where there are no organised gangs, there can be no gang wars. Organised gangs breathe suspicion; they drive fear amongst their peers. They taunt one another with war on words. They bully each other, and behave aggressively over drugs, money, and would-you-believe-it girls!

Nottingham-based Brother Daveed Ben Israel formerly of the African Hebrew Israelites had this to say on Radio Nottingham when asked to reflect on the gang wars between the youths of St Ann's and the Meadows.

> "We are warriors. The Creator made man to defend his family and territories. If we don't know who we are and where we are, we are going to do those things that come naturally; but we will do them for the wrong reasons, and do them in the wrong places".

Vanessa Graham, a St Ann's Sister of the Order of Rastafari (Honour and praises to Jah!) goes further into knowing one's self:

> "I feel these Black youths do not know their own culture. I don't think they like themselves enough to appreciate they're West Indi-

ans let alone Africans. They classify themselves as English. They live in a society where they are Armani! They are Nike! They are Moschino! For instance, take a pair of Moschino trousers: it costs roughly £110, likewise the shirt. They will do anything even steal just to wear these designer clothes. As for food, they don't want no yams, dumplins, banana or salt fish. Give them the fish and chips and the Mac Donald's and they'll be happy.

Certain societies from ancient times have used literature even the bible to propose the theory that Black is no good. This stigma has actually rubbed off on some of them. CHILDREN: WE ARE THE PRODUCT OF MOTHER AFRICA AND WERE THE FIRST TO BE BLESSED FROM CREATION! The same bible says 'honour thy mother', notice it says 'Mother' first — then 'Father'? Love yourselves and be not drawn into the self-hate concept that 'I'm no good'!"

As I sit at table in her front room taking notes, I invite her to try and link the 'crisis of identity' theory to the behaviour of our Black youths who are featured in gang wars between the local territories of St Ann's, Meadows, Radford, Basford, Sneinton and other city areas:

"Cocaine: this is where the youths are at. This drug was a product of Hollywood upper class society from as far back as the roaring 20s. The American C.I.A. and F.B.I. came together and held a big meeting in the wake of the assassination of Malcolm X during the 1960s after which they decided to meet the challenges posed by Black activist Civil Rights struggle. So they decided to target the Black ghettoes of the United States. They decided to let cocaine out on the streets in a big way for the very first time. I would like to invite you to try and get hold of a book I have read several times called "The Emperor Wears No Clothes" by Jack Herer. It shows that the 1960s cocaine trade was deliberately planned to mash-up Black people. This is a known fact! When cocaine gets into the bodies of these youths, it makes them arrogant and abusive. It makes them daring to the point of doing the most dreadful thing. When they take it, it gives them a boost. At last, it makes them feel they're somebody! Unfortunately, what they fail to realise is that this drug was aimed directly at them...to mash them up, slow them down, and make them brain-dead".

This sounds pretty much like the point of view posed by 'Pegie Man' Robinson of St Ann's when I spoke to him earlier:

"No Black man no 'av ship! No Black man no 'av no plane! No Black man 'av high-speed jet fe go bring 100 kilo a cocaine in a dis country. The Whites delberately let it out on de streets. A try dem a try fe mash we up. My friend, yu see dis ting ? All a dis is psychology. Pshchology fe mash we up. Look what it a do to de youth dem? It damage d'brain. Mash dem up! Dem a kill dem one another. Dis is madness!".

CONSPIRACY THEORY?

"Cocaine is definitely a trap... frankly, I feel if our Black youths were to stop and internalise the sort of politics that's responsible for stage-managing cocaine, they would probably want to stop before it got to the point of no return. The cocaine conspiracy started in American White society. Now it's being pushed upon the Blacks. After reading 'The Emperor Wears No Clothes' by Jack Herer, (1993), I am convinced the conspiracy is not just about class. It is also about race.

Vanessa Graham — A St Ann's Sister of the Order of Rastafari-

"Psychology fe mash we up...de Whites deliberately let it out on de street. Look wat it a do to de youth dem? It damage de brain. Dem a kill dem one a nother; dis is madness!"

He goes on to make a startling comparison with cannabis as he slaps his hand on the table with emphasis:

"Me will fight to de death fe legalise cannabis. Equally me will fight to de death to put a man behind bars fe smokin' cocaine.
No man nuh want no ganja. MAN WANT BAD BAD TINGS FE MEK DEM FEEL LIKE GOLIATH — cocaine!!! Locking-up a man fe smokin' cannabis is stupidniss. If my son smoke

'Pegie Man' Robinson of St Ann's

ganja I will join him, but if im eva come een a my house wid cocaine a ban im! I come een a dis country in 1957. I was a youth dem time dey. Same like Missa Gale, Sonny Bravo, Remel Smith, Melvin Downs, Alvin Mc Kenzie, Doctor wid im Sound System, Chalkie, Chick and Pretty an dem man dey.

Wen I was in Jamaica, my father's father used to boil tea wid ganja herb...strain off de ganja water an' bwile more tea again. Dem even bwile soup an ting. It mek yu feel good. Ganja a medicine me a tell yu! Good good bush bath wen de body full-up a pain. Een a de dictionary dem describe it as 'vegetable matter' just like Jamaican callalloo. Get real. It long time betta dan de tablet wey de family doctor dem a gi we fe mash we up".

Lorraine Mc Hale from the School of Nursing at the Queen's Medical Centre in Nottingham counters this by saying:

"Even if ganja was a form of help for those whose brains could take it I still would not encourage any youth to take the risk. I have known of loads and loads of young people who have ended up in mental institutions because their brains could not take substances like ganja, never mind the crack and the cocaine: all right for those whose brain can take it, I certainly would not encourage any youth to smoke it. I have seen my own sons smoking ganja and it makes them lazy, lethargic and lacking in self-esteem. I could never bring myself to condone ganja whether it be medicinal or not".

I can assure you my boys are not taking it for medicine. They are taking it for fun. For a start they come home late at night or early next morning, sleep whole day and if you don't tell them to get up, they don't. Right now one of them is being kicked out of college. Already he has lost several jobs. The ganja makes them feel good for a while I don't doubt it. But as soon as it wears off, the side effects begin to come. Those side effects leave them feeling drained and looking like zombies. To pick themselves up again, they will have to induce their bodies with more ganja again. Is this the way to live?"

Before I get drawn into a ganja discussion, I must hark back to what Vanessa was saying about cocaine. I will come back to ganja in the later pages. Actually, since my book is mainly aimed at the youths, it would be very good if one of the boys or perhaps both could speak to me. They might

even be able to offer a word about the practical side of ganja-taking.
Just to get back to cocaine what Vanessa and 'Pegie Man' are saying is that this particular drug was aimed by American White society, at the ghettos where Black people live...hence, the issue of race is rearing it's ugly head. Mr Robin Melville, information Officer at the Nottingham Alcohol and Drugs Team links cocaine not with <u>race</u> but <u>culture</u>. i.e. 'high-class culture'!

"Cocaine is culturally defined because it is more expensive than ecstasy and amphetamines. It's taken in sniffable form mainly by people who are more well-off".

Adds Kieth Hellawell, government anti-drug spokesman:

'The classic image of drugs problems being confined to youths in rundown areas do not reflect the whole picture'.
<u>"In a powerful message to middle-class parents, he said their well-educated children were probably taking drugs in nightclubs"</u>.

The following quotes, were taken from the Nottingham Evening Post 2000-02-01 page 2. Both these men are emphasising the underlying impact of cocaine not by emphasising race but culture.
From a Nottingham Evening Post report dated 12 Jan,2000 p2, it is clear that Nottingham has got a very bad reputation for cocaine. To continue Vanessa's trend of thought, the American experiment to target ghettoes and deaden the minds of Black people has at last reached Nottingham:

CITY'S COCAINE SHAME

"Nottingham has been named by Britain's drugs czar as one of three cities with a serious cocaine problem.
Keith Hellawell senior anti-drugs advisor equated London and Liverpool, with Nottingham in terms of drug problems..."

Another Evening Post report (30/12/99) highlights the Meadows area, citing children as young as 11 involved in selling drugs:

"'A boy of 11 dressed in trendy jeans and tracksuit top, wheels by on his push bike. He approaches a teenager, exchanges a few words and passes him a small package before riding off to meet up with his school pals".

But the truth of the matter is, it might not even be cocaine. It might be some other form of 'hard' drug like crack or heroin. Mr Karl White, the Leader of the Meadows Youth and Community Centre feels that there are youths who accommodate crack as a cheap substitute to the cocaine they might never be able to afford.

A lady in St Ann's says the crack dries out your inside. It makes your lips dry and makes your eyes look red and wild as though you have not slept for nights and nights on end. The worst is yet to come:

- Crack makes you sell your bed!

- Crack makes you sell your best suit!

- Crack makes you sell the last shirt on your back!

- Crack makes you sell the fridge and the video set!

- Crack makes you break into a car just to steal the radio!

- Crack makes you apply for a bank overdraft!

- Crack makes you compelled to beg, steal or borrow!

- Crack makes you sell your bum!

- Crack makes you sell your whole body because you are no good to yourself.

This lady told me she knew of a youth who actually cut out the bath tub from his upstairs flat, just so he could sell it to buy crack. Why?

Because crack is addictive.
Crack is a self-imposed punishment!
Crack is misery!
Crack is pain!
Crack is torturing you on the wrack!
Crack is drying out your inside!
Yet you must have it! You must!! You must!!! You must!!!!
Why?

- Why do we torture ourselves?

- Why do we belittle ourselves?

- Why do we destroy ourselves?

- Why do we agonise ourselves?

101

- Why do we drag ourselves down into the dust?

- Why do we dehumanise ourselves?

- Why do we debase ourselves to this level?

- Why do we allow ourselves to be enslaved by a man-made drug?

- Why do we wrestle with the better of our minds which is telling us no, no, no?

- Why do we under-value our abilities to rise above constraints like these?

- Why do we suppress the natural urges to do better?

- Why are we afraid of our 'higher' selves?

- Why is crack getting the better of our youths?

Because the youths are weak is that it?
Too weak to care?
But then, our 'higher' self never goes away from us. This is what Abraham Maslow is saying when he speaks about the 'real' self. The 'real' self or 'higher' self is always there inside us. The 'higher' self pleads and pleads and pleads!
The 'higher' self knows what is right.
The 'higher' self is the God-conscious state of a man, woman or child am I right?

There is a quote from a Nottingham Evening Post article dated 30/12/99 which demonstrates just how easy it is for under aged children to peddle drugs. Since it has now become so commonplace, nobody would suspect anything sinister:

"People on the street would not bat an eyelid. They will think it is just children playing", said Inspector David Shardlow, Commander for the Meadows estate. 'But the boy is selling drugs. He is selling heroin'."

102

LATE EVENING IN ST ANN'S

In a Nottingham Evening Post dated 20/12/99, Simon Redfern reports on St Ann's on page 18:

> "In St Ann's we know of toddlers who see parents using heroin in front of them, and they are raised thinking it is almost a part of everyday life".

Most evenings from 6:00 onwards when I walk past a little gathering of lads in my area, nobody can be quite sure what they're up to. Six or seven of them may be? What they are muttering is so discreet I have no idea what they are talking about. They mainly wear woolly hats, age ranging from about 15 to 20, and are White or mixed raced. By the time I get to the shop and back, the action begins to look busy when a bike or moped pulls up.

There is another action group mostly Black lads who form a core of their own. Their age group may range from 16 well beyond 20. The White group tends to hang around either a phone-box or a shop which installs a phone, while the Black group makes conversations on their mobiles. Oddly enough, there is hardly a girl in sight except for the occasional car which pulls-up with some dish of a nice young tart coming out of the back seat — legs, short-skirts and blonde! Before you know it, another car pulls up and she's off again.

Vanessa Graham seems to make sense of all I am saying. As I look at the problem of youth and drugs in St Ann's she chips in:

> "Police block-off end streets and put up ballards, so as to make it easier to keep-up with the youths and their drug pick-up points; but they are at a disadvantage since the youths have got widespread access to the use of mobile telephones".

Another woman living near the Robin Hood Chase, was telling me how she watched a sizeable gang of Black youths, hovering round and round the back garden gate of her house. They tried to gain access. She could see them from behind the blinds of her kitchen window but they couldn't see her; Putting two and two together, she suddenly decided to give them a piece of her mind, since she felt they had their fresh supply of hard drugs, and were looking for a convenient dump ground where they could discreetly store it:

"Unno clear off! Leave me back yard alone! If unno have sometin' unno want fe bury in a me back yard, unno go back a Basford, unno clear off! Me noh want no Police come a me house, unno clear off!!! !!!"

WHERE DO THE GUNS COME FROM?

Gun! Violence!! Shooting!!! Presuppose a nasty turning-point to the saga of gang wars in the Meadows, St Anns and Radford. Why guns? Why have guns come to feature so prominently nowadays surely it never used to be like this during the 1960s when I arrived from Jamaica as a tender 17-year-old? My cousin John Wray used to take me to these all-night shubeens at people's private houses. You could hear the heavy bass sound of blue beat coming from down in the basement. Aston and Palomeno in-the-Chase were two of the big names in them days. English girls were wining-up wining-up in front of Black guys and there was hardly a Black girl in sight — that's another story altogether but why? Nowadays, guns are coming into circulation at an alarming rate. Where do they come from?

The other day, a Radford Youth Man was telling me he was offered a gun for sale:

> "I walked into a pub in St Ann's, and a man offered to sell me a gun for £75. He claimed he had just killed a man in Ireland, and didn't actually need the gun anymore".

He was not keen on the idea. Frankly, he didn't want anybody planting Police forensic evidence on him. "Buying a gun is trouble", the brother-man said. Incidentally, I also spoke to Mr Karl White, the Leader of the Meadows Youth and Community Centre:

> "Getting hold of a gun is easy: I feel that one gun could be circulated to several parts of Nottingham. Once it's been used, it can be passed back to the borrower so it is passed on to somebody else. There are places that rent guns so there's another possibility! People break into gun shops and steal guns all the time. Actually, one of the quickest ways of getting hold of a gun nowadays, is from ex-Army Officers fleeing from war who no longer need the use of their guns; those fleeing from Bosnia provide a good example".

Mr Exie Bryan, an Afro-Caribbean formerly a resident in Nottingham (on the telephone from another region in the country where he now lives), highlights Belgium, Spain, Holland and best of all, France as common vantage points from whence guns can be bought and smuggled into

105

Britain. For the benefit of readers of this book who might still be asking 'where do the guns come from?', he is inviting us to consider the theory that the opening-up of the Euro-tunnel in 1991 is 'the root of all evil'!

"Think of it logically: the weapons accessible to Nottingham youths in street fights were either knives or baseball bats. But with the advent of the opening-up of the Euro-tunnel, notice how the whole trend has changed: guns start flooding our streets! How do Guns get into Nottingham? Realistically, there aren't many gun dealers in Nottingham. Guns for a start, can't come to this country on aircraft passenger flights because of the aviation industry and its 'restrictions on firearms' policy. For guns to get in, you have to have a licence so how do you work round that? — smuggling!

The shortcoming or 'chink-in-the-armour' arising out of the Government's Euro-tunnel policy goes like this: sniffer dogs are trained initially, to sniff out drugs. They are not trained to sniff out guns and armaments, so there we are! The 1991 Euro-tunnel is the root of all evil. Mind you, the government is now aware of what is happening although it's late. Also, current Euro-tunnel Security and Customs restrictions are now in operation to counter certain freedoms small traders used to enjoy. i.e. cheap wines and cheap tobacco".

'Pegie Man' maintains that a gun becomes a matter of prime necessity once youths begin to embark on the dangerous business of peddling hard drugs like cocaine. The gun is virtually the only protection they will crave for. With the new cocaine culture in force, these guns are a must: On the price range Vanessa chips in:

"Those who are in the cocaine business can pick-up a gun for £100, £200 or £300". Ownership of guns lead to the ownership of cars — expensive cars like 'Lexus'!"

She develops the point further when she says that the various All-Night Blues parties dominated by big sound boxes from down the Green (Hyson Green) during the 1970s have all closed down. Some of the big names that spring to mind as I write are Brummy, Beefy, Big Sam and Falk. 'Why have these clubs closed down? She answers by saying:

"Because of this silly business to do with cocaine. General members of the public who used to go down there to have an enjoyable night-out, used to be turned-off by this disgusting traffic of cocaine. The smell for a start... when you went into the toilets there was no access; the space was all packed-out with clients prospecting for their share of 'the rock'.

Lorraine Mc Hale from the School of Nursing Queen's Medical Centre in focusing on other aspects which have led to the closure of these clubs, opens-up on other factors when she mentions:

"Boom! Boom!! Boom!!! The loud noise of the heavy beat coming from the sound of the music was disturbing. The noise from the party goers, the cursing, the swearing, the fighting, and the jokes and de big laughs and the greetings with more and more noise up till all hours of the morning was too much for the neighbours to bear. Nobody gave them a thought. Not even the devil in hell would've been able to put up with all this bangarang! Lack of respect. That's what it is. Frankly, I am not surprised that they find it so difficult to secure a license to open a proper club".

Vanessa invites the reader once again to appreciate a shift in the Nottingham party-going night life behaviour in the 60s before the dawning of the horrors of this 'new' cocaine culture :

"Honestly, it never used to be like this in the 60s. When you went to a blues, you would expect to see a Black man with his little roll a'ganja. He rolls his spliff, carry on playing his cards or wining his woman in some dark corner. What does ganja do to ya? It opens your mind. You see things clearer. It helps you relax. When singers and poets use it, it helps them create good logic. Now all that's changed".

Lorraine holds a sombre and pessimistic view of whatever form ganja-consumption entails. What about those whose heads cannot take the stuff (?). It makes the brain lazy and lethargic.
Mr Spec 'B' the versatile Singer/Performer-Poet from St Ann's would no doubt support Vanessa on this. He says it increases the concentration span and maximises people's mental potentials. People who pursue more brainy jobs will experience great benefits. Lorraine in taking a sceptical

and corrective view of ganja puts it like this:

"One does not have to smoke ganja to open one's mind. If a person has a certain level of intelligence and self-esteem, he/or she does not need this thrash! My main aim, is to encourage and advise the young people to get a good education whether in terms of practical skills or University study skills. You don't need any form of drug to live above a certain standard. Personally, I would like to encourage some of our children to do their work experience just for a day in a Mental Institution, and they will see the damage for themselves".

It's kind of hard not to address ganja. As and when it comes up, I like to take the opportunity to air the views which people are offering. Before the pages of this book are finished, I hope it will be possible to hear from the youths themselves. Incidentally, Mr Roydel Youth Man is trying to facilitate a discussion between myself and the youths at the Karibu Hostel, for the purpose of an actual contribution to this book. In the meantime, let me allow Vanessa to close this little section with her final thoughts on the evils endemic to our present cocaine culture:

"At the moment the youths are running things to their own advantage. Their advantage is holding what you might call a "rave" to peddle and circulate drugs that are on the black market. If it's anything to do with the old days, the last all-night blues of any kind was the St Ann's Workshops in Bullivant Street during the early 90s and it had to close down why? Because of the cocaine and the 'new' gun culture. There was a shooting followed by a Police raid. Those days are over, that's it, no more blues. The guns are now on our very doorstep".

6 CITY SHOOTINGS
IN TWO AND A HALF WEEKS!

"THIS IS THE SIXTH SHOOTING IN THE CITY IN TWO AND A HALF WEEKS!"

This statement from the local Evening Post dated Thursday 3 Feb, 2000, p 2, is a reflection of the scale of violence perpetrated by guns alone. The same paper named a 26 year-old youth who was shot in the head, shoulder and stomach as he cycled along Abbotsford Drive in the St Ann's area on the night of January 16. A further shooting — this time a 22 year-old male of St Ann's, took place on 31 January. He was shot in the shoulder, by a group who came to his door and apprehended him. Both victims luckily enough, are now recuperating in the Queen's Medical Centre.

In another Evening Post report dated Sat Feb 12, Councillors Des Wilson and Jon Collins addressed a gathering of some 50 'concerned residents' of St Ann's. Councillor Collins said:

"Police are investigating six incidents where shots were fired in the St Ann's, Meadows, Lenton and City centre".

One of the obvious outcomes of this 'concerned residents' meeting, is an increased presence in terms of regular Police patrolling in St Ann's. Officers are frequently seen on horseback riding through and through the back streets. In consequence, a climate of fear is developing round the issue of personal safety. The answer in real terms is cited by 'Pegie Man' one of the concerned residents when he says:

"BY CLEANING OUT DE GUNS AN DE COCAINE, IF DEM DON'T DO SOMETHING ABOUT THESE THINGS, DEN SERIOUS TINGS A GO HAPPEN EEN A DIS TOWN"!

GANG WARS BETWEEN MEADOWS, RADFORD AND ST ANNS

In piecing together bits and bobs of house-to-house info, I am given to understand that the Meadows is a no-man's land or peninsular. A peninsular is a country surrounded by water. At the back of the Meadows are the pseudo-middle class of West Brigford so that the only place for the impoverished inner city youths to move is upwards towards the city belt and beyond.

It is the St Ann's and Radford youths who provide competition since they enjoy better facilities for hanging out in pubs and clubs. This helps to explain the push and drive of their peers from the Meadows who would equally like to have more pubs and clubs so as to feel an equal sense of pride.

Arising from all this, there is an understandable fear if a youth is going to take it upon himself to walk the streets outside the perimeters of his own territory. For safety reasons he will much prefer to walk with members of his own gang.

One Sunday night I visited a friend of mine in the Stanley Road area of Radford. She used to live in St Ann's. As a matter of fact, she had only just moved house and felt very worried about her 16 year-old son who much preferred to hang around the house. As soon as it turned nightfall he dared not venture outside. As far as he was concerned, this was Radford. He did not want to show his St Ann's face anywhere in the neighbourhood.

In real terms this is what it is all about. This leaves a somewhat unsavoury taste in the mouth doesn't it? Yet it is true... I definitely do not like the sound of this at all.

WHAT ARE THEY WARRING ABOUT?

My understanding as I am led to believe by Youth Man Roydel the writer of the Preface of this book, is that they are warring about:

<u>"Who makes a better job of fixing-up de ting real real good".</u>

What 'ting my lord? Everytime I ever had to tell somebody of my plight to research and put together a manuscript in a bid to try and explain some of the problems experienced by the Radford, St Ann's and the Meadows youths I am told it is something to do with:

<u>"Who makes a better job of fixing-up de ting real real good".</u>

My answer to that is if they were 'fixing-up de ting real real good' den they wouldn't have had to bother to fight at all – my guess is (lame excuse) they are doing the very best of a bad job.

"Baseball bat!"

Is that all? For a moment I thought they were going to be telling me something out of this world. What is dis 'ting my lord? At the end of the day it might actually turn out to be skunk laced with resin — O SO WE ARE TALKING ABOUT DRUGS after all.
SKUNK — sum nuff nuff respect to Youth Man Roydel the lead writer of the Preface — IS MORE DANGEROUS THAN BROWN WEED. Brown weed is the fresh product from the natural earth whereas skunk is a man-made concoction incorporating all sorts of chemical wastes from other substances like crack and heroin.

<u>"Who makes a better job of fixing-up de ting real real good"</u>

in real terms, is translated to mean which territory sets up the drug (s) in such a way as to 'lift-off'. i.e. keep the phones buzzing! buzzing!! buzzing!!! whilst clients keep coming for more! more!! more!!! For instance, most of the folks I have spoken to on one-to-ones say the Meadows youths have got a dramatic sales technique. They pile-up and pile-up and keep the customers waiting. Then when the big influx of floodgates come down, they suddenly drop the price which is EXACTLY

WHAT THE CROWD LIKES. So when the same crowd comes back for more they UP THE PRICE-bow!wow!wow! yes sah!!) Funnily enough, they don't mind paying.

> "Nottinghamshire Police local area Commander Inspector David Shardlow said 'about 100 people are coming into the Meadows area each day and getting drugs. Heroin can be bought for as little as £5'".

If this wasn't true how did Inspector Shardlow get hold of this information? See Evening Post dated 30 December, 1999, page 18.
The people who will be coming back, as crazy as it may seem, will be more than willing to empty-out their pockets all the more reason if the drug is peculiarly addictive. At my neck of the woods in St Ann's, I am told flatly that the smallest piece of cocaine rock costs £40. Heroin would normally be in the same bracket. Hence, it may come as a 'surprise' to realise that one can secure a spot of heroin spliff down the Meadows for only a fiver. £5 is normally associated with the likes of cannabis.

When I recently spoke to Mr Carl White of the Meadows Youth and Community Centre, he was of the view that some of the youths who were turning to crack, were doing so mainly because they were finding it difficult to keep up with the price range set by cocaine dealers.

● burgle a house just so you can get hold of a few household items to sell

● smash the car window in order to get the radio and sell it

● sell your prized coat or best pair of shoes

● or just beg, literally beg in the streets

● anything from £1. Within a day you might raise the £20 for a small spliff or the £40 for a bigger slice of the action.

AND THE SORT OF MONEY THEY MAKE?

"Round about summertime 1999 Police raided a house in St Anns and found that <u>a 15 year-old boy, had £12,000 underneath his bed</u>".

<u>TWELVE THOUSAND POUNDS?</u> (comes from very good source; subject of newspaper coverage and all that). Towel? Scrub yu bowel?? I give up. <u>TWELVE THOUSAND POUNDS??</u> Sey wa? This gives you an idea doesn't it? The parents O my Lord! By the way the Court can't send him to prison, he's too young — The parents:

- struggling with the mortgage!
- struggling with the gas bill!
- struggling with the electricity!
- struggling with the Severn Trent water bill!

An dis likkle bit a bwoy... he is 15; this is it. Gives a rough idea of the sort of money drug peddlers make right here in Nottingham. Gang wars (in my opinion) just to give a break-down, <u>are not necessarily based on</u>

"<u>Who makes a better job of fixing-up de ting real real good</u>",

but

"Which territory or turf makes a better job of turning-out the big money".

<u>As I see it, it is the money which is helping to fuel the hate, the envy, the suspicion, the feud and bad blood between the youths</u> of Meadows, Radford and St Ann's. One guy just to give an example of the sort of money he used to earn them years ago when he was selling de ting claimed he made.
"Thousands of pounds within days".
Hang on, hang on, hang on what did I say he said to me?
"Thousands of pounds within days".
Roydel Youth Man used to wear below waist-length Armani khaki-looking coat fitted with long pockets. Late nights or wee small hours of 2:00

and 3:00 a.m. when he used to come home to his house his pockets were loaded. Padded and rammed? That's it. Padded and rammed with money.

By the way, the life of this said youth has changed over the years. Frankly, he is not into drugs anymore. Nowadays he has spiritual ideas of mind-regeneration and mind-rejuvenation. When he meditates, he does so without the prompting of drugs of any kind. He searches for the Creator within his 'higher self'.

MONEY: wrong or right this is my theory. If this is the key to understanding the escalation of gang wars between the Meadows, Radford and St Ann's, the worst thing, just about the w-o-r-s-t thing that could happen is when a guy turns up from outa town and does very very well for himself. Six years ago, an outa town Youth Man unfortunately got himself knifed to death down at the Marcus Garvey Centre, when he was involved in a fracas with other youths.

Up till this day, people maintain that he was well loved both in the St Ann's and Radford communities. He was particularly charming to his girls and good at making friends across the divide. The main thing that possibly could have been held against him was the fact that he came from far beyond the fringes of Nottingham. However popular he became, people still tended to see him as an 'outa town' guy.

WE TURN THE VIOLENCE ON OURSELLVES

BECAUSE
WE ARE TOO FRIGHTENED TO FACE THE REAL ENEMY
by Bunny Richards/ former Political Activist for the B.P.F.M.
(Nottingham Black People's Freedom Movement)

Those youths who are not old enough to remember the B.P.F.M. at Canning Circus — top of Derby Road — your parents will. During the late 60s and 70s, Hyson Green Youths could not afford to fight those from Sneinton, and those from Meadows couldn't afford to fight those from St Ann's why? Because we were too few in number. We had to unite to survive. As Blacks we understood how to stay together and think of ways of dealing with the common enemy. And what what was the common enemy?

- Racism

- Capitalism and

- The forces of social control

On a Saturday morning when we used to meet up at the Old Market Square to chant slogans of 'freedom' — 'when do we want it? Now!!!'-with our base ball bats and all sorts of milk bottles in our pockets, the Police and general members of the public understood what our concerns were. For a start:

- There was no Meadows or Sneinton Community Centre, neither was there any A.C.N.A., Marcus Garvey or Hyson Green Boys' Club.

- None of us as Blacks was granted a Public Licence to open-up a social club. In fact –take a trip with me to 'memories lane' — the only person who had that privilege was Carlton Forbes. Put it down to the fact that he used to play for Notts County Cricket Club. That was why it was easy for him to get the licence to open Calypso Club.

The Whites would not allow us in their night clubs. The only two night clubs that granted limited access to Black people during the 60s were the Dungeon and the Beachcomer re-named 'Ad-lib'. Twelve of us had access, and I was among that number. Guys like Carle Montgomery, Franklin Hall, Morris Mead, Parker, Dennis, Thomas and Seymour will know what I am talking about; so will Junior Forbes (Berenge Bandele)!

Hence the birth of the 'shubeen' was a direct result of blatant racism. With the 'shubeen' there was no licence to sell drinks or blurt out music from the sound system. We were basically running the risk of more confrontations with the Police. Those who held private house parties on a Saturday night were equally liable to get raided by Police. Big names which were running 'shubeens' in the Robin Hood Chase were Aston and Palomeno. The same trend continued during the 70s when guys like Brummy and Beefy opened their clubs on Radford Road Hyson Green.

During the early 70s, there were times when I had to call upon the Meadows guys to come and help me deal with White boys who were attacking Black boys in the city mainly at nights after pubs were closed. An unwritten rule went like this:

The worst –just about the worst thing — a Black youth could bring himself to do, was walk the streets on his own. If there were two of you, it was bad and bad enough.

The White youths singled us out for easy targets the moment they saw two of us walking together after pub closed at 10:30. UNDER THESE CONDITIONS, WE HAD NO CHOICE BUT UNITE. THAT WAS THE ONLY SENSIBLE THING TO DO.

From the level of the B.P.F.M., we decided on co-ordinated action: for real THIS MEANT UNITY! UNITY AMONGST OUR YOUTHS BE THEY FROM SNEINTON, MEADOWS, RADFORD OR ST ANN'S. Under the banner of the B.P.F.M. this effectively meant all of us coming together to form an army.

Arnold Wright: I can't think of anyone who does not know Arnold Wright –the guy wearing the spectacles and the dashiki shirt He, along with Le Roy Wallace, emerged as architects of the Ukaidi Community Link Project on Woodborough Road. During the times of the B.P.F.M., Arnold was nicknamed the 'Field Marshall'. Instructions came from him. Anything to do with aspects of organised response in the wake of violent encroachments on our rights, we knew exactly what to do. The B.P.F.M. at that time, was named the second most militant Black organisation in Britain –seconded to the Black Panthers' organisation from London's Ladbroke Grove.

So formidable had we become that Police watched us everywhere we went as a group. For instance, they accompanied us every week-end

116

whilst bus loads of us went en route to the Spider's Club in Clifton; when club was over, they escorted us back to Nottingham thereby ensuring that we were peacefully disbanded to our respective homes.

Hence, my question to the present youths of St Ann's, Meadows, Radford is this: where is our unity? Is it the fault of our parents, or is it the fault of the type of society we ourselves have created? Is it something to do with the 300-year period of slavery endured by our foreparents? Are we still afraid of our old colonial masters? Are we afraid of them in so much that we are prepared to wreak vengeance on ourselves? If this is what we are doing, then surely, it must be a sickness! A sickness emerging from out of an equally sick society who were actually bent on equating us with the beasts of the field.

When you take away a person's language, you take away his/her entire culture. He/she becomes a dummy. He/she cannot express his/her own fashion, painting or music. All of that has been annihilated –even our names are gone from our consciousness so we end-up as, Bill Black, Jack Red, Fred White and Sam Brown.

"The word 'negro' in Greek is translated 'necro' which means 'dead'".
from the Anthony Browder File of 22 Essays (1989) page1.

Death, in the eyes of the Greeks, is actually applicable to a mental condition. That of zombies. Our recourse through the forms of healing, for a start, cannot come through drugs — sorry mate. Those who seriously think that the ganja is going to be the panacea to all our ills need to think again. Agreeably, it may have started out as a holy drug but things have gone wrong along the way: for instance, we have ended-up eating meat, drinking cow's 'milk and enjoying a whole lot of fizzy pop loaded with carbon, phosphoric and malic acid plus the caffeine (in the pop) which is damaging to our system. Frankly, our only recourse is through education, enlightenment and awareness.

A man who is aware doesn't kill his own brother. No sooner than you kill your own brother, you find that you need him to help you fight the man who is calling you 'necro' meaning brain dead! No sooner than you kill your brother, you find you need him to help you fight the unequal distribution of poor housing conditions, unemployment and deteriorating relations with the Police.

Both I and Pitman Browne came to this country from Jamaica in the early 60s. And from what we have learned from guys who were here long before us, it would seem as though the 50s was an unparalleled example of unity amongst us. You need only to talk to people like Pegie Man, Country, Cock Topie, Blipper, Pretty and Doogie! Frankly, our present youths have got a lot to learn. I hope things will be on the upturn soon.

ECONOMIC PROSTITUTES!
NEW COCAINE ORDER

In my research/discussions withVanessa Graham, a St Ann's sister of the order of Rastafari (Honour and praises to Jah!), I have become aware of a new type of prostitute who is put on the streets with the sole purpose of making money to feed, support and reinforce the new cocaine culture. In other words, the old days of the economic prostitute, are almost at an end:

"Times have changed a lot since the 60s and 70s. A woman had the choice. A woman today still has the choice to do what she wants. The flesh trade — since I am talking about female prostitution — was dominated by a workforce of women who sought to make money purely for economic reasons. She wanted to make money to make ends meet. Some women were sent out on the streets by men. The collecting point years ago here in Nottingham, used to be the 'Tally-Ho' where men met women, collected their money and sent them out on the circuit again. Other women made the choice to work purely for themselves alone. A girl might try to 'do a thing' purely on her own steam just so she could find enough money to pay the rent, electricity and gas, as well as buying food for her and her child (if she had any).

Nowadays, a female prostitute fulfils an almost different job description since she is more likely to be caught-up in the 'new' so-called cocaine culture. People on the Council (those higher up... don't look so surprised Pitman, I know wot I'm saying) are actually engaged in sending women out on the streets of Nottingham to make enough money to feed their cocaine habits. For prostitutes the times are different 'cos the generation is different. Cocaine culture is in fashion nowadays".

At this point, I stopped writing for a minute and disclosed to Vanessa my sense of surprise if ever I had to be walking past a couple o'girls hanging out on street corners from midnight or wee small hours of early morn. They don't seem to look frightened. They don't look as though they want to sleep. Most girls no sooner than it gets to 10:30 at night, will make sure they are in bed where it's nice and safe. She assured me that practically all of them were on cocaine. Cocaine gives the personality a boost; that is why they don't look frightened.

"Me fren? No prostitute noh een a no cocaine. No yu wrong... Dem don't like the stuff".

These are the words of Youth Man code named 'T fe Terrible' as I talked with him in his front room at Radford. Whilst jotting his words on note paper I went on to ask: 'If prostitutes don't use cocaine, what stuff do they use to keep them going?'

"'Special Brew' and 'Tennants'! Dem feed de habit wid de drink".

Youth Man Roydel totally disagreed with Youth Man ('Terrible'):

"That is rubbish!!! I used to feed prostitutes on Forest Road wid drugs. De Creator has changed my life; I don't do dem things no more cos I'm a new man. DE GAL DEM LIKE DE COCAINE. Dem gal who noh tek de cocaine w' prefer fe go pan heroin and alcohol. De trouble with this is some a de gal dem lie! Dem don't want people fe know sey dem a tek cocaine.
If a gal mek £50 fe d' first two hours, you can bet between £30 and £35 a go pon cocaine. If not cocaine, den dem a go tek heroin mix-up wid de Extra Strong Tennant".

Youth Man Roydel is actually correct regarding the aspect of secrecy. Some prostitutes tend to be very very secretive on the whole issue of drugs never mind cocaine. About 20 years ago when I used to live in a multi-rented house on Burns Street near Forest Road, one of the tenants — a White girl — liked to boast about the loads of week-end money she used to make as a prostitute. Her philosophy was simple:

"If a man tells me I am beautiful... if he tells me he needs my body for his satisfaction... if he goes to the extreme of wishing to reward me with money, I don't think it's right that I should turn him down".

One day an ambulance came and took her straight to hospital 'emergency casualty'. It wasn't until days following her discharge that she informed us that an emergency surgical operation was carried out in order to pump drugs out of her. I certainly did not know she was on drugs! In fact, in all the time she had been boasting she had never ever mentioned drugs once.

120

Coming from a prostitute, this is the sort of oral, on-the-spot material I would consider relevant to this book. This girl was proud of her body. Proud to be solicited by men. Proud to be of service to them. Proud to be a recipient of the money. She assured me above all, that she was not sent out on the streets by anyone. She worked for herself. As it happened, she was unemployed also, therefore, the money came in handy.

Mind you, I had a feeling she was glamorising everything. While talking to her, the sorts of key questions kept springing to mind were:

- What if you were my own sweet little sister?

- Sweet sister where is your self-respect my dear?

- Where is your dignity?

- What if your parents spotted you on the game?

BLACK GIRLS
IN THE PROSTITUTION TRADE

"Between one and two o'clock one night I was walking from St
Ann's to Mansfield Road; this Black girl in her trainers/designer
gear was sitting on a wall along Cranmer Street... started speaking to me straight away. Believe me, I was absolutely impressed
by the intelligence of her speaking voice. She was softly spoken
and seemed so relaxed as she sat imbibing the fresh night air. She
comes from a stable family background; it shows on her!'

By the way, she asked me my name and I told her. I asked her
her age and she said she's 19 and has a child. There was something
about her. Maybe it was the smell of... men usually buy an expensive body lotion called 'Lynx' costing over £40 wow this girl really
smelt nice man! I felt ever so embarrassed since I didn't have any
money in my pocket to give her. As a rule I don't walk late nights
with money in my pockets. This is because 17 years ago I suffered
the indignity of being attacked by about 6 White youths after midnight; they wrenched all of my money from my pockets as I walked
'short-cut' through the Forest Grounds... anyway that's water
under the bridge now... I said b'bye to this beautiful prostitute of
a Black girl and guess what?

About six weeks later I saw the same girl while walking past
Cranmer Street up Mapperley Road. This time,I had money in my
pockets so I gave her £10. She asked me if I go to church. Obviously, she was shocked when I told her I wasn't interested in 'business'! She asked me which church I go to and so forth".

I explained to Vanessa that I needed to try and compile statistics reflect-
ing the actual percentage of Black girls involved in prostitution here in
Nottingham.

"If you want to go back to the 60s, a small number per capita of the
population has actually made it. In Nottingham I can think of the
name of at least one Black woman who has succeeded in buying a
house and paying the mortgage out of prostitution. This was during the 60s when there was hardly a Black prostitute for miles and
miles around. On the Nottingham scene Black prostitutes didn't
really get off the ground until the 70s. When we say prostitutes

don't forget we're not just talking about those who hang about street corners. Some prostitutes work from home with the help of the magazine advert columns and the telephones. Those tend to make more money. Sometimes they are required to travel out of town even as far as the Continent.

For a Black girl, Germany is the best. Forget about the issms and all the racisms under the sun. German men not only like Black girls but are prepared to offer a high price for them".

I told Vanessa I was baffled to know that <u>out of all the Black girl prostitutes I have spotted in the streets of</u> Nottingham, I had never seen Black guys accosting them for business. Always White males. To put it another way, could White males be prone to valuing Black girls more? Do they value them because they're genetically different? Hard to say. Then again we are not actually talking about love.

We are talking about prostitution. Girls are supposed to sell their bodies for money. There is no love in this business. No glamour. No feeling. This is the way it works in the flesh trade.

My friend Bunny Richards recently put me in touch with a Nottingham-based organisation called Prostitutes Outreach Workers (P.O.W.) and I put the same question to the Project Director, Susan Johnson:

"By the way I am pleased Pitman that you have taken the time out to come and speak to members of Staff at P.O.W. about your plans for your new book. In the light of that, I would be happy to share or at least give my viewpoints since you have asked. The point about Germany and so forth... I agree that there is a huge demand for Black prostitutes in that country. Again, if I were to answer your other question to do with the numbers of Black girls into prostitution here in Nottingham, I would say the figures are unclear. Judging from the questionnaire form I gave you the other day, there is a head count in progress at the moment to do with gender, age and race. The results of that won't be made available for our office records for another 6 months or so.

To come to your other question about the low count of Black males approaching Black girls as clients, I take each situation as I find it. Arguably, the German situation is a bit more like grand textbook statistics. I am not saying it isn't true that Black girls do exceptionally well in the trade in Germany.

My view is more to do with a practical day-to-day perspective of life as I see it as I walk along Forest Road whatever time of day or evening. Or better still, St Ann's. I live in St Ann's. Prostitution sometimes grow out of mixed relationships between Black and White partners. That is why it is often difficult to tell who does what to who. (?)

The POW project was started in 1991 when two prostitutes, Susan Johnson and Maureen Mc Donald trained as researchers and outreach workers. The overall aim of this Nottingham-based Organisation, is to provide advice on aspects ranging from legal aid, family planning, health issues, housing accommodation and education.

POW maintains a neutral and non-judgmental stance in the sense that they are not telling prostitutes what to do with their lives. Rather, they provide confidentiality, an open door as well as a listening and understanding ear to anyone who seeks help and advice. Here is a sample advice page — quote-on-quote — from pages 4 & 5 of their 'Possibilities for You', booklet:

Prostitute Outreach Workers Project

Learn how to:-
speak another language or sit some GCSE's or other qualifications.

If you want to do it - you can !!!!!!

It's possible you may come up with one of these excuses for not considering college or re-training schemes:-

You say: I haven't got the time, I'm already working.

We say: You can **MAKE** time if you really want to - you deserve time to do the things you want to do.

You say: Who's going to look after the kids?

We say: Lots of colleges and training providers now offer childcare - ask at POW.

You say: I hated school - why should I go back to something I hated?

We say: You had to go to school. You had to learn what you were told to learn. This time, you'll make the choices. You'll say what you want to learn when you want to learn it.

You say: I earn a good living from prostitution - why should I change it?

We say: You can earn a good living from another job, and nobody's saying you have to give up prostitution, but girls can you do it forever, what about the future?

You say: Are you trying to stop me working as a prostitute?

We say: NO, we are not. We're trying to offer you a choice for the future. You can go to college and work - it's up to you

125

PROSTITUTION AND
THE ROLE OF BLACK MEN

This is what Marsha Barnes had to say about Black men's role in the Prostitution trade:

"Very rare will you see a Black guy approaching a Black girl offering money for sex. Black guys, if it's anything to do with the prostitution trade, act mainly as pimps. When was the last time I rescued a girl from off the streets? — Only last year! Where from? Forest Road: at first when the Spirit of the Lord led me to pray around the streets, I didn't want go since it was night; moreover, it wasn't exactly warm; so when I put on my heavy top coat and went to Forest Road, there was this pretty17-year-old girl with tears in her eyes. I asked her why she was in the trade, and she asked if I could walk with her for a bit. I noticed she kept looking behind us, so I asked her who she was looking for. "My boyfriend, he is hiding in the bushes". "Where is he?", I shouted. "Please!!", he'll beat me up!!! This really outraged me, I was so angry.

Here is an ordinary Black youth no more than 18. They fell in love, and halfway through the relationship, she was influenced into living off immoral earnings just so he could smoke loads o'weed and buy himself a pair of Rebok trainers and what have you.

I told her to come back to my flat with me, so we could talk. We sat down over a cup of hot chocolate with whipped cream, and she shared her dreams of becoming a hairdresser. I then encouraged her to get a college prospectus and enrol on the course. That night we exchanged phone numbers and I sent her home in a taxi. Later, I spoke to both her mother and grandmother on the phone and they confessed they had no idea what their girl was going through. They didn't even know she was a prostitute. The irony of the story anyway, is that the girl went back to this guy. This time, he held her hostage for several days whereby she was subjected to beatings. He was even burning her with cigarette ends; so the parents asked me to intervene. The Police was called…in the end the parents thanked me….

An experience worse than this, takes me to Leicester where I was on a week's visit from Nottingham. This other girl was 18 with

126

brown eyes, brown hair and heavy brown eyelashes. She came from a wealthy family and Pitman, if you heard her speak you would know she was of middle class background. When I got to Leicester, the Black guy treated me like an Honoured Guest.

But the way he treated this girl my gosh, something inside me moved: It's the fear in her. Her eyes told me the whole story. From this guy she had nothing but fists straight to her head, and all over her delicate young body. Not even time for a decent meal. Every day, pressure, pressure... <u>She had to go out on the streets to earn 300-and-odd £££ of prostitution money even if she didn't feel like it.</u> She hadn't the moral courage, my gosh she didn't have the guts to stand-up to him and say <u>no</u>! <u>no</u>!! <u>no</u>!!! (let alone keep back a single penny). She had to give him everything. '<u>Good heavens no</u>', I <u>thought to myself, this girl does not</u> deserve any of this'!!

I persuaded her — for the time being — to hide some of the money in her boots. Furthermore, I suggested even if she wasn't ready to go back to her parents, she could secure 'emergency' accommodation in a bed-sit or rent a room somewhere until she decided what she wanted to do. It worked, it worked!! We planned something and within days she had packed her bags and left.

Up till this day, the guy has not challenged me. For some reason he just didn't bother to ask me about her 'dramatic' disappearance. Mind you, he knew I had something to do with it".

Youth Man Roydel on hearing Marsha's experience of this girl snapped:

"Sympathy? I don't have sympathy to dish out. I am not saying the guy isn't responsible an so forth. In de prostitution trade it teks two. Nobody can force any gal fe go out on dem streets. It teks two. Two cannot walk together unless dem agree. If she no want fe go out there, nobody can make har. Nobody can make har stand out there in snow, fog and pouring rain! <u>This gal</u> — my gosh — <u>this is har</u> <u>own body</u>. We are talking about har body here. A gal in her right mind? If, she allowed herself to be dragged into dem slackniss, den she has to tek some a de blame for har suffering. <u>First of all did the guy put her on dem streets, or did she offer?</u> We don't know. If he put har out dere, den dat was wicked. Where? Where?? Where is her anger??? Where is har self-respect???? Har self-respect is har '<u>real</u>' self, and har '<u>real</u>' self is har self-respect. Where is har pride? Where is har dignity?? Where is har self-esteem?? How come she hadn't made even as much as an attempt to get out of dis situation?"

O.K, O.K.! Marsha is not saying the girl isn't equally responsible for being involved in prostitution. What she is saying is that there are Black men out there who are violent. They give their women hell. They will send them out on the streets; they will even beat them if they didn't want to go out there. Let me bring Marsha back.

"The first time I actually set eyes on this 18 year-old, was when she, me and the guy were travelling together in the car to Leicester. What made me realise she was a prostitute, was when she started changing into her tights and short skirts. The true extent of her suffering became worse by the day. I now know that I must have gone to Leicester for two reasons: 1) to see for myself, and 2) to render moral support where it was most needed. Yes, she needed it badly, and I am glad I was there for her. What I am basically trying to say to readers of this book, is that there are girls out there who are weak... all of this wonderful dignity and self-respect is locked-up inside them; yet, for all of this, they are weak... just too weak to stand-up to their man and say no! To stand-up to somebody — remember — you've got to be in the right frame of mind. IF YOU ARE NOT IN THE RIGHT FRAME OF MIND, YOU WILL STAY IN SLAVERY AND SUFFER, BLEED AND DIE IN BONDAGE! Yes Roydel, I hear what you say: self-respect and self-esteem and that. Look at it this way: Even if the girl screamed 'blue murder' and the authorities came to her assistance, she might still be living in fear that one day whilst going about her own business, she is accosted, attacked and beaten by the same man. Things like that can happen you know?

Youth Man Roydel questions the girl and the awful sacrifice she has to make when she decides to surrender, relinquish and give-up all claims to her own self-will, self-respect and self-esteem. In his eyes, she looks like a fool. In Marsha's eyes, this girl is overcome by the spirit of fear; in that sense, she is much too weak to think for herself.

Let me put another scenario to the readers of this book: given that 'love is stronger than death' — cards on the table — how do I know there aren't girls in this world who would be prepared to go on the streets ALL BECAUSE OF THEIR UNDYING LOVE FOR THEIR MEN? How else can you explain the behaviour of <u>girl number</u> <u>one?</u> <u>Girl number one</u> was rescued on Forest Road from the awful hands of a cruel and despicable 18 year-old guy:

"My boyfriend is hiding in the bushes!! Please, he'll beat me up!!!"

<u>This girl with tears in her eyes remember? For God's sake why? Why</u> <u>does she find it in her heart to go back to him after all Marsha Barnes</u> <u>has done for her? I can't answer that! Youth Man Roydel can't, I can't,</u> <u>not even Marsha can?</u> When I say 'love is stronger than death', this is no more than a theory (?). Nobody knows why this girl is silly enough to go back into the hands of a man who has been reducing her to the lowest common denominator — that of a common prostitute — she alone knows why! In that case, one can hardly blame the man now can one?

This is the position of Leslie Robinson formerly of Barry Ward and Griffith's Solicitors: he takes the view that the role of pimps <u>is not</u> <u>endemic to Black men at all</u>. If the Press is malicious and racist enough to feed us with that kind of tripe year-in-year-out, we will end up believing it. <u>OK, where does the pimp culture comes from? It came specifically</u> <u>from out of the English street culture that dominated the slave trade.</u> <u>There are 'strongly-based' historical reasons why a certain type of White</u> <u>woman will want to come to a Black man — even now — and offer her</u> <u>services on the streets... During slavery, prostitution was introduced on</u> <u>a mass scale when the English Government allowed Irish women</u> <u>(nicked-named 'women of the lower orders') to go to Jamaica 'purely for</u> <u>breeding purposes' now this is true! This is true also of the lower orders</u> <u>of Scottish women. Consequently, those Black men who actually become</u> <u>involved in the trade as pimps, you need to be speaking to them so you</u> <u>can understand what transpires between a prostitute and a pimp</u>.

Whilst talking with the Project Director of P.O.W., I put to her the point made by Vanessa to the effect that she thought White males were repressed sexually, and the text of the repression would run like this: 'Thou shalt not have too much sex', and 'thou shalt not have too much children', and 'thou shalt not go over the top' etc.

"A valid point about taboo! This might have been the situation in the context of a 50 or 60 year-old White male living in a little village somewhere outside of town say 20 years ago. I am not saying that these taboos don't still exist, but things have changed a lot. Time has changed. The present White males from out of the housing estates of Radford and St Ann's are of a different world.i.e. today's world!"

On that note, I took the opportunity of thanking P.O.W. for actively participating in terms of viewpoints and opinions. I asked Susan Johnson/Project Co-ordinator if I could also have the privilege of incorporating a few quotes from young prostitute clients who have actually written big 'thank you' notes in the pages of the P.O.W. Annual Report 1998/99:

"I think P.O.W is a great help, if it wasn't around I don't know where I would be now. I was involved in prostitution, and addicted to crack. I wanted to stop both. P.O.W. helped me get away from both of them. I have been clean for 2 months, and I've also stopped working in prostitution.

P.O.W workers are all there for help and support for everybody for all kinds of issues. P.O.W. is now helping me get into college in September, and also working towards me valuing myself,and the things I do. I am really glad P.O.W. was there for me; I know they'll be there for anyone else"/female /age:18

"I just want to say thank you to everybody at POW who has supported me through my bad times, and helped me get my life on the road again. If it wasn't for POW, I don't know what would have happened to me. They have done so much for me. They have helped with my decorating, and helped me with my reading and writing. Most of all, they have helped with my drug problem. POW is a part of my life now, and I can never forget what POW has done for me. So I want to say a big 'Thanks' to Sue, Mo, Wendy and Tina, for being there for me in my times of trouble, and to help me through the hard parts of my life.

Nuff respect –God Bless you all, from someone who is very grateful for your help and support.
— *female*

And while we are on it, let me end this section by incorporating the general synopsis of an interview which took place at POW's Office with the helpful co-operation of a client. You will notice that the above mentioned clients from the POW Annual Report 1998/99 remain anonymous. As Author, I will respect anonymity especially in relation to the next client.

"WITH HELP FROM POW, MY LIFE HAS EXPERIENCED A GREAT CHANGE ESPECIALLY SINCE THE LAST THREE MONTHS!"

"At the age of 14, Teacher called me in the Staff room and told me: 'you won't amount to anything; You won't amount to much more than a prostitute'. It didn't get a year before the Teacher's prophecy was brought to fulfilment".

At the age of 15, X started hanging out at street corners, back streets, by the side of pubs or even near bushy parks with clustered trees where she could easily disappear with a client.

"School didn't do a thing for me. That place didn't do me no good 'cos I was branded 'disruptive' or 'chatter-box' whatever they want to call it. Frankly, I just talked and talked and didn't know when to stop. I seemed to, get in everybody's way. But it wasn't all me own fault an that, 'cos me home life for a start was in a right mess. By the time a was 14, me mum had split-up from me dad. So me dad said I could come an' stay with him. The only trouble is, he was too heavy on the ole disciplinarian stuff an all that. To correct me, it wouldn't take anything f' him to shout me down, slap me down or clubber me one! To tell you th' truth, it was beginning to get to me, so I left home you understand wa' am saying?"

My, my, this girl talks man, she really does talk! Incidentally, what I found so absolutely amazing about her as I listened to her in the Guest Room at POW, was the honesty with which she balanced out her story. Society is largely at fault if a School Teacher can find it in his/her own heart to prophecy doom and gloom on somebody else's child. Unfortunately, this is a sad commentary on the system if a Teacher is allowed to condemn a student to a miserable life on the streets? Howard Becker, the American Sociologist is absolutely right when he warns society against the effects of self-fulfilling prophecies administered by those responsible for teaching our youths!

Incidentally, what I totally commend this girl for is the honesty with which she unloads her story. She never tells it without finding space to criticise, analyse or even find faults within her self: just look at the way she zooms in on herself:

"Frankly, I just talked and talked and didn't know when to stop. I seemed to get in everybody's way".

Self-examination is a kind of cleanser yes? Mind you, she seemed a bit hard on herself. Once she began to open-up on the theme of drugs, it became clearer that the school environment was really to blame:

"I went to two comprehensive schools in Nottingham, and de ash an de weed was available like nobody's business. By the time I left school, I was well into de drugs scene yu understand wa' am saying?"

For the benefit of readers especially those who are still at school, listen to this... she is analysing the effects of crack:

"Crack just made me want to sit in the house and mope. Crack made me feel frightened. Crack made me feel afraid of the real world outside. Crack put a damper on my inner spirit. Crack made me feel depressed. To get any kind of buzz out of crack, you had to have a regular supply of money just so you can feed the habit".

Two or three little ounces of crack, according to Youth Man Roydel, might cost £20 to £25 a time. The buzz lasts only 12 minutes!

"O WHAT A WONDERFUL CHANGE MY LIFE HAS MADE!"

Her facial countenance reflected a kind of natural radiance as she spoke. At one point I had to say to her look:

> "Right now your eyes are sparkling; I am sure you couldn't have looked like this when you were on crack".

> "You're dead right", she added.

She went on to disclose that from the day she walked into POW's advice surgery, things began to change little by little. Another factor that was proving of great help, also, was the influence of a Pentecostal Black-led Holy Ghost Spirit-filled Church:

> "All these people were standing to their feet and saying, 'O what a wonderful change Jesus has made in my whole life!' They were saying things like 'whatever is your need, Jesus can help you tonight!' Mr Browne, it became easier and easier for me to terminate a life of drug addiction which had literally held me captive for all these years".

Finally, I put it to her that she had at long last discovered her 'real' self, whereupon she admitted that her new found freedom was actually attributed to the intervention of POW, coupled with the influence of the Church. I asked her to enumerate the ways that POW had helped her:

> "They give me a chance to catch-up with reading and writing skills... I come in one day a week for that. They also let me come in as a volunteer one day a week. Also, I've got great news for you. I have passed my exam in communication skills, I have got my certificate at home".

Thank goodness what a beautiful change, I too am glad!

WHY DOES ANYONE
WANT TO BECOME A PROSTITUTE?

Okay look at it like this: why does anyone want to drink cows' milk? Just to get the calcium that builds strong teeth, strong bones and helps preserve good eyesight etc? If one wants calcium why doesn't one just go to the veggies shop and buy a packet of raw sesame seeds and eat them the same as raw peanuts? Why have people got to wait for milk from the cow in order to extract the calcium it gets from the grass and grain?

Why does anyone want to become a prostitute? By waiting for cows' milk to be processed by big time profiteering manufacturers, one is rendering one's self liable to picking-up all sorts of deadly bacteria once the manufacturers start adding penicillin and other anti-biotics . Could it be that the reason people continue to be prostitutes is that they enjoy the risks — what the hell? Like manufactured cow's milk, you only need drink it once before your system starts asking for it again and again?

On a dark windy night when a prostitute is standing in the cold and rain, each prospective client might be saying 'no not tonight luv'. From my reading of Abraham Maslow's theory of self-actualisation, I am given to understand that human needs never ever stay the same. Some needs outlive their usefulness quicker than others: for instance, once you have been there, seen the good side of making quick money, and the bad side

134

of being apprehended by a Police, you will start wondering if there are better ways of making a living without all of this hassle.

"The child who is bored with the delights that he has savoured sufficiently, goes on to higher, more complex delights as they become available to him without danger or threat".

Toward a Psychology of Being" (1969) p55-56/by Maslow

"Goes on to higher", is the key to what Abraham Maslow is saying to his readers. In other words, 'is there more to life than being a prostitute? The prostitute after careful consideration might end up saying yes!

TWO

IMAGINARY

FACES

OF

A

PROSTITUTE:

PENCIL

DRAWINGS

BY

Paul Michael

Berwise-Ebanks

WHY MYRNA'S FACE LOOKS SO RADIANT
(subtitled: PROSTITUTE TURNED STUDENT)

Myrna's face looks as though she is teaming with radiant sun-filled emotions –the sort of emotions we experience when we read, listen to in-depth music, study, meditate or pray. Frankly, you only need to reflect on those highly exalted states of facial expressions experienced by Diana Ross in her 1970s film "Lady Sings the Blues". Charles W.Leadbeater calls them 'summerland vibrations' in his book "The Astral Plane" (1987). Perhaps what he is trying to say is that the emotions arising from the lower orders of sexual greed, envy and hatred, cause stress and psychic depression whereas with the onset of radiant sun-filled emotions, we tend to bask in the joys of expanding consciousness.

- Myrna's face looks ever radiant because she is always reading journals to glean information about the lives of famous Fashion Designers.

- Myrna's face looks ever radiant because most Saturday mornings she visits the gym down at Heathcoat Street in the Lace Market for a good physical fitness work-out with disco music in the background.

- Myrna's face looks ever radiant because when she doesn't show-up at the gym, she is located at the swimming club down at Victoria Leisure Centre near Sneinton Market.

- Myrna's face looks ever radiant because she is sometimes found in the Aboretum Park with her board carrying out charcoal or pencil-drawings of trees and tops of buildings.

Pencil drawing by Paul Michael Berwise-Ebanks

WHY MARVA'S FACE LOOKS ALL STRESSED OUT
(Subtitled: PROSTITUTE SEARCHING FOR HER 'HIGHER' SELF)

Charles W. Leadbeater in looking at the human mental states identifies 7 planes — the highest being the heaven world of holy fantasies, and the 7th being the lowest of the lowest which is loaded with cursing and swearing, since it is corrupt, earthy and devoid of all notions of appreciation. (See chap 2 of 'The Astral Plane'/1987/ Leadbeater).

Abraham Maslow in 'Toward a Psychology of Being'/1968, creates an even clearer hierarchy model when he presents a triangle with 5 tiers, the lowest being the most basic of our animal needs. Sexual needs are enumerated as one of these needs. The highest need — number 5-which he locates at the very top of the triangle, is the point of "self-actualisation" or knowing ones inner self.

- Marva's face looks all stressed-out because at 20 she has not yet sorted herself out in terms of 'the respectable and legitimate job market' — in other words, she is unemployed.

- Marva's face looks all stressed-out because the only identity that makes any sense at the moment, is the prostitution-related identity, and she has to struggle to keep the money coming in.

- Marva's face looks all stressed-out because all day long she can think of nothing but sex in order to fulfil her financial objectives.

- Marva's face looks all stressed-out because of the fear of competition with other prostitutes. She has got into fights once or twice for standing on their turf.

Pencil drawing by Paul Michael Berwise-Ebanks

138

PERTAINING
TO
ISSUES
TO
DO
WITH
MENTAL
PROBLEMS

MAD, BAD OR SAD?

Dr Chris Udenze

Black or White, young or old, most of us will suffer from our mental health at some time time except you of course! You probably think:

"Bwoy dem tings will nevva 'appen to me. I ain't soft in de head, I can tek de pressure, I don't need no shrink or counsellor; me, I can deal wid it all myself".

Over the last 20 years — by the way, greetings one and all — I have seen a lot of patients who couldn't deal with it all, some get low, can't sleep, get wound up and lash out, get stressed, diggy, hear voices, think they are Christ, etc.

My father is from Nigeria, my mother from Ireland, I grew up in South London and trained as a Doctor at Guy's, the local Hospital. For the last four years, I have been a G.P. in what White Planners call 'the inner city' St Ann's, Nottingham.

Let me explain to you how Western Medicine sees mental health. Mental illnesses are seen as either:

Psychosis which is 'major', the most common of which is schizophrenia, or

A Neurosis which is 'minor' the most common being depression anxiety, etc.

Medical treatment is based on a clear diagnosis — which is made by talking with the patient. i.e. taking a history. There are talking treatments. e.g., counselling, psychotherapy, etc, or drug treatments like anti-depressants, anti-psychotics and tranquillisers.

So how does this Western psychiatric model deal with the needs of Black people in a racist society? Not very well but we can still make the best of a very imperfect system. Getting a diagnosis is often straightforward and sometimes not, but is a useful start. A brother who can't sleep, does-n't want to eat, feels negative about the whole world, may well realise he is depressed if he'll admit it to himself or open-up to someone, and can then understand why he is feeling so negative.

STATISTICS CONNECTING BLACK PEOPLE WITH SCHIZOPHRENIA

Nottingham is infamous for a survey which seems to show that more Black people have schizophrenia than Whites. Was it that White psychi-atrists were wrongly diagnosing Black patients when they were just responding to stresses in an extreme way, or was it really more common among us? Schizophrenia is surprisingly common.

About 1% of the population will develop it — 1 in 100 people that you know, usually in their 20s. Even though some of us ending up wrongly 'labelled' — some of us certainly develop this 'strange' condition. Usual signs of this condition are:

- Feeling paranoid

- Having bizzare thoughts

- Having hallucinations or,

- Hearing voices often to a very distressing extent

POSSIBLE TREATMENTS:

Like I have said before, there are 'talking treatments' for schizophrenia e.g. Cognitive (thinking) Therapy, but it is difficult to know how well they work. (?)

There is a drug called chloropromazine. For your information, it takes the form of a long-lasting injection, tablets or a syrup.

Then there is dipixol, another drug which is designed to lessen voices which might be telling you to kill yourself, kill somebody, rob a bank, set fire to someone's property, do violence or rape somebody.

These drugs, if they don't work, can produce distressing side effects like shaking hands, shuffling gait, rapid weight gain, drooling, etc.

Now there are newer schizophrenia drugs, which are massively more expensive than chlorpromazine but have less side effects. Often Black people get high doses, or the more toxic anti-psychotics, and White people are probably more likely to get the new atypicals Clopazine and Olanzepine.

Any drug treatment should just be part of a package of care, which should address all aspects: housing, education and employment.

IN TERMS OF MY OWN RESPONSE...
By Pitman Browne

Along with all other respective contributors who have hitherto been assisting in making these pages more informative, let me take the opportunity here and now of thanking Dr Chris Udenze for sharing some of his medically-related thoughts on issues to do with Mental Health.

As Author, I would like to assure readers that any research into possible types of available treatments that can be administered in the face of our mental problems, is worth time and effort. In a nutshell, this book takes the view that those who find themselves in dire straits and deeper waters (i.e. nervous breakdowns), are prone to suffer much more if they are having to think gosh:

"I don't flippin' know who the hell I am;
I don't know why the hec I'm here — why?"

Probably because one's personal self-concept and self-esteem lays buried under the morass of year-after-year soul wounds, and all these mountains of unpleasant memories may never ever be moved or eradicated unless one is willing to take the necessary steps to clear and unblock these kinds of 'dysfunctional' characteristics. People can unblock their own 'dysfunctional' mental states... by their own self-healing efforts yes? The more good strong images we can muster at our disposal, the better our chances of mental survival in this uncertain world.

The saying goes 'when we are down, there is only one way to go and that is up'. I have carefully read what the Doctor has been saying about the types of treatments on offer for mental illnesses, and have come to the conclusion that drugs are not reliable. The Doctor has put both sides of the coin, so the reader can appreciate that chlorpromazine injection or depixol tablets may well confer side effects such as shaking hands, rapid weight gain, drooling and withdrawal symptoms like talking to one's self and/or laughing to one's self.

MY BELIEF IN PSYCHOTHERAPY AND THE COGNITIVE (OR THINKING) FORMS OF HEALING:

Dr Udenze in making use of the term "Psychotherapy", is actually explaining "psycho", the Greek for mind, and "therapy" (in Greek "therapeia") which pertains to any healing process which can be appropriated. Just to answer the question, 'how can one receive healing from the effects of mental ills?' My own answer is this: 'the mind can heal itself, possibly, without any form of drug whatever'. I shall come back to that in a moment.

"Cognitive", is also pointing to the mind and its capacity to think, store away information and gather new information. Just as how I have got the capacity to over-eat — now I am talking about food in the belly — my mind has got the capacity to attract and overload itself with all sorts of material it doesn't really need. For the moment I would like to appropriate terms like "psychotherapy" and "cognitive healing" to suggest that I — or should I say 'we' are blessed with the self-regulating capacities to wind-down, unload, discharge, unblock, neutralise and clear our minds of all the fuzz and unnecessary luggage that is getting in the way.

WE CAN SHUT DOWN THE MIND!

Yes, we can shut down the mind. If we really wanted to, we could acquire enough control over our own mental states to shut down the mind when it is getting overloaded to the point where one feels one can't control one's thoughts anymore. There is no such thing as 'I can't help it'! One can control one's own mind, O yes, I believe that. More often than not, that ability is locked away somewhere in the higher self. P.D. Ouspensky in "A New Model of the Universe (1997) p256 says:

"Unnecessary thinking is one of the chief evils of our inner life".

HOW DOES ONE SHUT THE MIND DOWN?

In my second book, "Wishing Can Be Dangerous" (1999) pages 141-143, I have offered a very tangible example of shutting down the mind and bringing it to a standstill, so it becomes clear and focused in one direction — the direction you want it to go! That way, I can actually exercise full control over what I want to think, so I am able to leave out all the luggage and garbage and interferences that's likely to make me depressed. To do this, one has got to be in a place preferably one's own bedroom where all is quiet and still. The best healing for your mind is light — got it? Light; why?

Because the mind is wonderfully created from fire atoms. Forget about the brain now... the brain is just a mass of physico-chemicals, whereas the mind is not. The human mind is certainly not a 'natural' phenomenon no?? The mind is a mass arrangement of... wait for it... SUPER-NATURAL FIRE ATOMS WHICH CAN TRAVEL FASTER THAN THE SPEED OF LIGHT got it? WE FANTASISE ABOUT PEOPLE ALL THE TIME. SUCH FANTASIES CREATE SUPERNATURAL FIRE ATOMS. WHEN WE GO INTO DEEP DREAM SLEEP, WE ARE ACTUALLY WATCHING FIRE ATOMS AT WORK... FIRE ATOMS COMPRISING NOT JUST THE FANTASIES WE CREATE, BUT THE GHOST ('ASTRAL') BODIES THAT VIBRATE AROUND US BOTH IN OUR SLEEPING AND OUR WAKING! WE CAN TELL IF PEOPLE ARE CONDUCTING HIGH LEVELS OF MEDITATION AND PRAYER... THEIR FACES JUST SEEM TO GLOW LIKE A LIVING FIRE!!! THEIR FACES GLOW WITH THE FIRE ATOMS OF PEACE!!!

NOW SHUT DOWN THE MIND!!!

Just lie on a bed as I have explained in "Wishing Can Be Dangerous" pages 141-143. Pull the sheets over your head. Try not to go off to sleep, or that would be a waste of time. You are going to be bombarded with endless strands of thoughts coming from all over the place but try...... just persevere. Close your eyes. Try your very best to FOCUS ON ONE CLEAR OBJECT, AND THAT OBJECT MUST BE IN THE FORM OF FIRE! It could be a circle in the midst of which there is a little ball of fire. The fire must get bigger and bigger as you get closer to it.

Since the mind is made of fire, it needs another fire from out of the unknown regions of our imagination so we can draw some of its brightness, illumination and health-giving radiation.

According to the pages of my book, I was supposed to be laying in bed from about 7:am on a cold dark November morning. It literally took me hours to settle down and clear away all the fuzz and unwanted material so I could settle down with the sun. I looked straight into its brightness yes? As I got closer to the brightness, it actually began to look like a great lake of fire, and I began to feel fearless. Since I was unemployed, and didn't have anywhere to go, I wasn't bothered about time. By midday my breathing patterns became slower and deeper. Then my voice box began to change into a deep rich tone. My blood — yes — I cold feel lively sparks of 'healing' fire permeating the whole of my blood stream good heavens! As the day wore on, I could feel powerful gusts like fireballs of radiation just lighting-up the whole of my inner body so I felt good, good, good!! In fact, I ended-up screaming gratitude (albeit to the 'Powers-That-Be)' responsible for creating the sun, and endowing me with the capacity to use my imaginative energy to its fullest extent.

At 3:00 in the afternoon when I got out of bed, I felt totally in command, totally at peace, totally in control of my memory and above all, I felt as though I had found the 'real' me. Frankly, this is the point implicit in any study of Psychotherapy as a healing method. Having said this, this is only one amongst a whole range of self-healing techniques which I could personally recommend to anyone who is going through the throes of mental turmoil.

With drugs, there can be no concept of certainty; in practice, trial and error is more in tune with the goings on of day-to-day life as we know it. I have gathered from a friend of mine, that there is one other form of treatment which mental hospitals have on offer i.e. E.C.T.

MY DOUBTS ABOUT ELECTRO CONVULSIVE THERAPY
POPULARLY KNOWN AS E.C.T.

E.C.T. is a term for electrical 'shock' treatment administered to the patient's brain. Electrodes are actually attached to the head. This technique was invented by the German Brain Specialist Professor Hans Berger. Again, there is no guarantee that electrical shock treatment therapy will serve the interests of the patient, since the technique does not go as far as the psychological (or mind conditions) but limited rather to the brain and its physical operations.

Only a few days ago, a friend was sharing a really sad experience of a Black woman in her late 30s who was a close associate of him. At first she was prescribed drugs as an in-patient at a local Psychiatric hospital. Then it was decided that since there was no progress in her mentally depressive condition, the only recourse would be electro convulsive therapy. After acquiring signed and written permission from members of her family, the Psychiatrists proceeded with the course of treatment.

Unfortunately, it didn't work. The young woman was becoming worse in the sense that she started suffering from memory loss. In terms of speech skills, her reflexes were becoming slower. The beautiful spring in her steps had gone. She was now beginning to look lethargic in everything she did. She was seeming to tire easily. As soon as she became

146

weary, she would just flop in a chair... and that would be it.

The guy whilst telling this sad story, seemed to cling tenaciously to whatever memories he had of her before she was ill. For a start she was a Social Worker, one who was endeared to all the children in her care. She loved life, she liked a good laugh, and... something more about her... she was qualified in her academic life. GCSE's, A/levels and diplomas.

At the end of the day it may be too late. Or perhaps it will be that much harder especially since the E.C.T. treatment has already taken its course. Still, you never can tell... it'll take a miracle to bring her back!

DOUBTS SURROUNDING A FEMALE-RELATED DRUG CALLED PROZAC

Same friend again: this time he was talking about a young Black woman in her 20s, as it happened, a member of a local church. She went to seek advice from her Pastor. If I am hearing it rightly, she claimed she was seeing devils. Her fears grew worse over time. In the end she went to her G.P. who recommended specialist consultation with a Psychiatrist. The Psychiatrist in turn, prescribed Prozac with the hope that it might help to alleviate her disturbed mind, and bring peace.

No it wasn't to be! The young woman started feeling disoriented and fearful. She virtually could not walk alone. So acute was her fear, that she needed someone to accompany her anywhere she went; from time to time, my friend would offer to accompany her to the shop just to buy a loaf of bread and a bottle of milk. In terms of personality, she seemed to 'curl-up' like 'little-girl-lost'. At times she sounded as if she was drunk.

MY FRIEND THEN MADE AN APPEAL TO HER!!!

"Please", he urged, "don't take any more of those Prosiac tablets!" She listened, thank goodness, she did as he pleaded. As it happened, she had only one day's dose of her Prozac prescription, and thankfully, she has now given it all up. At the moment she is coming round slowly. It might take a while. What I am pleased about in the mean time is that she is willing to listen, and perhaps take good advice.

This young woman really does need to learn to listen to her own inner voice — not the disturbed voice that's telling her she is going to burn up in hell fire... SHE REALLY DOES NEED TO LISTEN TO HER OWN

POSITIVE VOICE. HER POSITIVE INNER VOICE IS HER GREAT-
EST ATTRIBUTE. IF SHE LISTENS TO THAT, SHE WILL COME
ROUND SOON ENOUGH!

MALE SUFFERS CARBON MONOXIDE POISONING

Years ago, a young Black male suffering the effects of carbon monoxide
poisoning was brought into the Psychiatric ward where I worked. I was
also aware that an acute absence of oxygen caused him to lose his mind.
At times he flared up into tantrums leading to violence; on normal occasions he would be more like a child. He was also suffering from brain
damage. This youth has actually attempted to take his own life.

Incidentally, I am now calling on the Mental Health Profession or better still, the Government to try and identify or pinpoint the underlying
reason for this kind of behaviour. Need not I repeat that 'the absence of
oxygen caused this guy to lose his mind' — hence, oxygen-deprivation is
a serious problem in our society today: what are we going to do about it?

The human body is a tool which is designed to function at the behest
of the mind. For the body to be at its best, it will help if the mind is also
at its best. If a patient is admitted into hospital suffering from the effects
of carbon monoxide poisoning, let alone, or to make matters worse, an
acute shortage of oxygen, then questions must be asked: are the causes
purely organic or are they social also? For instance, inner city carbon
monoxide poisoning is rampant not just in young males but females;
sometimes they try to seek an answer by turning to drugs. By the time
the hospital gets round to administering its own diagnosis, the ailment
is already to advanced and complex.

When there is a lacking in respect to the supply of oxygen, a person
cannot act on his or her own volition; somebody has to think for him/her.
Consequently, the dignity of the common man is gone, so is the spirit and
the wonderful privilege of independence.

In closing let me register an appeal in the face of deficient Government
Policy by inviting a more imaginative and creative approach to analysing
and treating the mental ills that dog our society. In the end perhaps it is
more research that is actually needed!

Anthony Robinson /Philosopher/Photographer/Performer-Poet

MY FATHER WAS DECIDEDLY DISCHARGED FROM A MENTAL HOSPITAL BECAUSE I INTERVENED!

(The identity of the person submitting this case history, will be remaining anonymous.)

'Sometimes a whole house can be full of people, yet you are lonely', have you ever heard that expression before? Well this was the sort of situation my father was in. As children, most of us had grown off his hands...now, we were adults in our own right. He didn't need to fuss over us and come to school to sort out problems on the playground between us and our playmates or tell off the teacher for showing us up in class. Those days are over. Dad is a very lonely man. We only see him as and when we commute between cities. We may catch-up with him on an occasional weekend visit; after we are gone, that's it.

I came back on one such week-end after a long stretch of weeks and found to my amazement that dad was not there...... where was he? My sister told me he was taken in to the Mental Hospital — you what? Mental Hospital Whatever For? Well this is it you see; with mental illnesses you never seem to get a straight answer. I dropped everything and went straight to the Mental Hospital only to be told that the Psychiatrists had diagnosed him in the shcizophrenic category which he honestly did not fit.

When I looked on dad he had a wide expressionless stare in his eyes. That beautiful sparkle and ruddy mischievous look had gone. So was his appetite. Just the look of the place alone was enough. As soon as the bell was rung, he had to be lining-up in a queue all ready to get his medication hand-out. I called for a meeting immediately whereupon I was told I had to come back the following morning. The question I put to the Senior Psychiatrist the following morning was why? WHY WAS MY DAD HERE? The Senior Psychiatrist in turn called for a meeting with the GP, Social Workers and other Psychiatrists. They agreed his condition was deteriorating so they let him out on grounds of suffering the effects of NEEDLESS INSTITUTIONALISATION — that's my point!!! We took our dad back home and now he is on the road back; in fact, he is making good recovery!

HOW

DO

DRUGS

FIND

THEIR

WAY

ON

THE

STEETS

IN SUCH

LARGE

QUANTITIES?

INDIVIDUALS
COMING THROUGH AIRPORTS

"According to drug enforcement officials, the United States face a new wave of drug smuggling involving Nigerian "heroin swallowers" backed by organised gangs".
The Guardian Index 1990, page 500

"A Nigerian woman who attempted to smuggle 84 packages of a drug believed to be cocaine through Heathrow Airport, died on September 22, 1992 after two of the packages burst inside her". (S) *S 23-18:1*
The Guardian Index 1992, page 497.

"Nigerian woman drug smuggler who had swallowed 111 packets of cocaine, died in an English hospital on 9 November, 1992. She was the 3rd mule to have died in five weeks after packets of drugs burst in her stomach. *(M) N 10-1, 6:7.*
The Guardian Index 1992, page 497.

However convincing all of it may seem, sorry mate, this is foolishness. By the way, I am sorry to hear that these two women have lost their lives but the question 'HOW DO DRUGS FIND THEIR WAY ON THE STREETS IN SUCH LARGE QUANTITIES' still remains unanswered. To be honest, we are talking about massive operations involving huge trafficking of cannabis and cocaine. Perhaps aircraft passengers like these two women are just isolated cases of people walking through customs at one time or another. Many of these people end up getting caught. Stories like these are a standing joke. They don't go far enough. With the advent of well-trained sniffer dogs and airport zoom lens cameras which can see right through the human body, I doubt very much if individuals coming through airports would be foolish enough to take the risk of being whisked away by airport officials once the alarm buzzer goes off. At the end of the day, if drug pushers in the alley ways of Meadows and St Ann's don't know how drugs came to be amassed on their streets in such large quantities, then somebody higher-up must know! What about top businessmen? What about the unnamed drug barons of the underworld? What about Politicians — yes Politicians! What about key representatives from the glamorous world of show business? Whichever influential people in 'high' places we may wish to name, what about them? What about the higher echelons of our own Police force? This country has had its share of corruption within the ranks of the Police. General members of the public cannot just sit back and hope that sectors within the ranks of our Police system are not involved in the large-scale trafficking of drugs from overseas contacts. We would well be advised to research this matter if it is ever going to be adequately substantiated. For instance, comfortable fireside talks pertaining to Police malpractices just won't go the distance. The language of the street all too often has been dismissed as poppycock why? Because nobody is willing to stand on his/her feet and articulate the source (s) of these claims — here is a good example:

A Sheffield man told a Police Committee of which he was a serving member:

"THE MASS INFLUX OF DRUGS ON OUR STREETS WILL NEVER EVER STOP UNLESS YOU YOURSELVES DECIDE TO STOP SUPPLYING".

I challenged this man — incidentally he now lives in Nottingham — to shed light on such an absolutely horrendous claim, and he simply went blank — so there we are! Then came my next question: did he tell the Sheffield Police Committee where he got his information from? Mind you, it took a lot of guts, in the first place for him to do what he did! I feel if the Committee decided to take legal action against him, he would probably be well able to stand-up in Court and defend his claim.

IS POLICE CORRUPTION PARTLY RESPONSIBLE FOR THE MASSIVE SUPPLY OF ILLEGAL DRUGS?

O.K. let's turn to the Times newspaper dated 5th February 2,000. Page 10 provides readers with some strikingly convincing answers to this question. For instance, Detective Constable "One" made confessions in open court at an Old Bailey trial to the effect that each time he carried out a raid and seized large quantities of drugs, he would re-cycle it in the market for sale. He admitted doing this for five years. Altogether, he admitted 16 offences of supplying drugs on the streets of London.
A second defendant in this drug-supplying drama — a woman identified as a "Super grass" Informer, confessed to 21 offences of supplying drugs.

152

The court was told that the Police Officer to whom she was assigned to supply Information, was in fact, her lover.

In Police circles, the term "Handler" is used to describe the Officer to whom the Informer must report on a day-to-day basis if needs be, while a supervising Officer of Higher rank is identified as "Controller". He is the one who issues instructions to the Informer as to what his/her level of involvement must be in the actual crime.

POLICE GIVES HER SEIZED DRUGS: SHE SELLS IT THEN SHARES THE PROFITS WITH THE POLICE!!

The court heard how she alerted her Handler each time she made a big breakthrough in the drugs underworld. The Controller would then sanction the raid to go ahead. After the operation was finished, she would be the recipient to whom the seized drug would be given, so she could then go out and sell it on the streets — amazing isn't it?

I identify this with another newspaper scenario pinpointing Police corruption to the tune of:

> "Drugs were re-cycled all the time. If you found 15 kilos of coke, you produced 12 kilos, and three would be sold. A kilo of coke, you get £30,000 so you have made £90,000".
> ©The Times Newspaper Feb 25th 1997

Believe it or not, this was part of a 'sensational' allegation which an ex-Policeman was making against Scotland Yard's Regional Crime Squad during the 90s wow wow wow anyway, — back to the story of the woman of a "Super Grass". Like I said, she stood in the dock at the Old Bailey in January this year charged with 21 offences of supplying, while Detective Constable "One" was charged with 16 counts of supplying.

JUDGE WAS APPALLED AT POLICE CORRUPTION!

As both of them gave evidence, the whole Squad was in trouble. In fact, these were the words of the trial Judge:

> "If Police turn to crime, then the whole fabric of society is affected".

The Judge attacked Senior Officers of Police for failing to stop a Detective Squad in London running out of control. The woman was sentenced to four and a half years, while the D.C. received three years and eleven months, the Judge pointing out that 'were it not for the level of frank confessions received, they would have got themselves 14 years each — good gosh! 4 years instead of 14 years? I find this absolutely disgraceful. This means they must've been laughing all the way to the Old Bailey and back.

   As a result of this case, the whole Squad was disbanded!! A court case like this helps members of the public to understand and appreciate which sector of society is responsible for the mass supply of drugs in our communities. In Jamaica, there is a well-known saying. i.e. 'what yu don't know yu don't know', but in this dear sweet isle of England, they put it another way:

"What you don't know won't hurt".

To be truthful, it does hurt when one has to sit down and uncover information to do with the mass circulation of drugs in our communities and on our streets. On the surface, these allegations against the Police are so dammed difficult to prove. Even when you SEE IT IN PRINT, it still is hard. I must say, I was pretty 'shaken-up' when I read in the earlier excerpt (the Times 20, Sept 1998) that Police Commissioner Sir Paul Condon had launched a wide-ranging enquiry into Police corruption, and had proceeded to setting up C.I.B. "3" (Complaints Investigation Bureau) to look into complaints of Police corruption. All this had come in the wake of an ex-Squad Officer describing Scotland Yard's Regional Crime Squad as:

"The most professional criminal cartel that Britain has ever produced".

To put it in the actual wording of the newspaper quote on quote:

"Drug rackets worth millions of Pounds were run from inside Britain's biggest Police Force 'according to a former Scotland Yard Detective who is to publish his allegations in a book which he proposes to write' ".

A note outlining copyright identity of newspapers from whence quotations were taken:
© *The Times dated 5 February, 2000*
© *The Times dated 20 Sept, 1998*
© *The Times dated 25 Feb, 1997*

SHOULD GANJA
BE LEGALISED IN BRITAIN?

THE GREAT GANJA DEBATE!!!

STORM AS
ANTI-DRUG
CHIEFS GO
SOFT ON
CANNABIS

STREET NAMES FOR HERBAL CANNABIS

Provided by Dr Miriam Stoppard in "Drugs Info File"(1999) page 44

Marijuana
Whacky Baccy
Spliff
Draw
Grass
Puff
Ganja
Herb
Green
Bud
Skunk

AGAINST GANJA!
Lorraine Mc Hale of the Nottingham
Queen's Medical School of Nursing!

FOR GANJA!
Vanessa Graham — a St Ann's sister of
the Order of Rastafari!

BALANCING BOTH ARGUMENTS:
Mr Spec 'B'
Performer-Poet/Singer/Graphic Design
Artist!

"What does ganja do to ya? It opens your mind. You see things clearer. It helps you relax. When singers and poets use it, it helps them create good logic..."
Vanessa Graham

"One does not have to smoke ganja to open one's mind. If a person has a certain level of intelligence and self-esteem, he/she does not need this thrash!
Lorraine Mc Hale

My aim in these final pages, is to facilitate as many viewpoints as can be aired and articulated within the framework of the great ganja debate. You will note for your information, that the caption overleaf headlined: 'ANTI-DRUG CHIEFS GO SOFT ON CANNABIS' was recently photocopied from the front page of a leading National Newspaper. In other words, the debate is in progress right now, and since there is a gradually rising spiral of interest in our own community, I feel it would be most appropriate to invite two of the contributors to the pages of this book to debate it.

By now, you will already have been acquainted with some of the opinions and views of Vanessa Graham, a St Ann's sister of the Order of Rastafari (Honour and praises to Jah!). She is absolutely convinced that cannabis — the Jamaican variant more popularly known as 'ganja' — is medicinally speaking, a safe drug to take. Some youths in her opinion, need to be re-educated so as to arrive at a proper understanding of its use. If not, they will use it at the wrong time, in the wrong way and end-up making wrong judgements about it.

Lorraine Mc Hale in her capacity as Nurse from the Nottingham Queen's Medical School of Nursing, takes a totally opposite viewpoint in the sense that no parent in his/her right mind should condone the smoking of such a drug, since it encourages a socially irresponsible attitude, as well as enhancing the likelihood of admittance into a mental institution for treatment. Right now, I wish to invite them both to come forward and set the tone of the debate. Afterwards, I will take the opportunity of inviting others to participate. First of all Lorraine please:

Lorraine:
Thank you Mr Browne. My aim, is to encourage and advise young people to get a good education whether in terms of practical or university study skills. If we remain in tune with our 'real' selves, we

won't need any form of drug to live above a certain standard. Every parent wants good for his/her child. No parent would want to see a child ending-up as a zombie. Personally, I would like to encourage some of our children to do their work experience just for a day in a mental institution, and they will see the damage for themselves.

Vanessa:
No. It is not the ganja that makes them ill. More often than not, it is the pressures of:

- Being in a peer group.

- Finding enough money to dress in a certain way.

- Keeping up with one's own friends.

- Wanting one's own space whilst living under one's parents' roof.

- Persecution or downright bullying, from one's work place.

- Difficulties in finding a job.

- Or perhaps the pressure of having too many irons in the fire at the same time... 'biting off more than you can chew'... people get 'snowed-under' with work all the time.

These pressures come from around us, and the w-o-r-s-t pressure of all –don't you forget –is the emotional pressure that comes from one's love life especially if things aren't working-out very well!

Lorraine:
Under the circumstances, just about the w-o-r-s-t course of action to take then, would be to turn to ganja. With a banned Class 'B' drug carrying a maximum penalty of 5 years imprisonment, one is not doing one's self-esteem any favours. Those who do not use banned substances, have no need of living in fear of a Police raid. It is terrible when a youth (some youths don't care), or parent most of all, has got to live with the fear that Police might come and demolish the front door with a sledge hammer, all because of ganja weed. My message is don't! Don't smoke it!!

And speaking of health issues, I know loads and loads of young people who have ended-up in mental institutions because their brains couldn't take it. Suppose your head is not strong enough to handle the ganja? Well don't! Don't take it!! Simple isn't it? Even if ganja made us feel good for a while, how do we account for the side effects that leave a person looking like a zombie?

Vanessa:

Ganja, if smoked in its proper context can bring one on a higher level of self which is peace. Smoking at college is the wrong way to go about it. You can't expect to work on computer with head full'a ganja. You will fall asleep. Common sense isn't it?

Lorraine:

But why smoke ganja in the first place? Why smoke it?

Vanessa:

Ganja is for when you are ready to wind down after work and study. Ganja offers herbal meditation.

Lorraine:

If one wants to go into herbal meditation, all one needs to do, is set a hot bath and pour lavender and basil oils into the bath. Switch off the light in the room, then light your perfumed candle, and what do you get? You get a sweet sandalwood aroma. One could lay in that bath for hours. The peace we look for, can be induced providing the herbal setting is right. The bad thing about ganja is, it makes one hallucinate. The spirit of peace cannot come through when one is hallucinating.

Vanessa:

That's where a lot of people go wrong. Pure ganja does not make one hallucinate; What makes one hallucinate, is when the pure ganja is laced with wastes from other manmade chemicals. This is what they call 'skunk'. Skunk is a mixture of wastes from crack, cocain or heroin. This is what makes the smoker hallucinate. Pure ganja does not do any harm to anyone. All it does is offer relaxation and inner peace. If you are an artist or poet, it opens-up your creative power. <u>What the youths of today need is re-education in the art and practice of this holy herb. It's been blessed from Creation: 'Let the earth produce plants bearing seeds' comes from out of the book of Genesis.</u>

Lorraine:
But if the same Genesis also says the ground is being cursed with thorns and thistles, then it invites me to put to you that something is definitely wrong with the ganja!

Vanessa:
What about pears and apples and oranges?

Doreen:
What about them? Are you asking if they are cursed as well? No they are not.

Vanessa:
The other day a guy wanted me to spend quality time listening to him. As it happens, he was suffering from a mental breakdown, and was also smoking his ganja spliff. <u>This guy said ganja did not bother him in the least</u>. He went on to unload some of the social and emotional pressures which were bothering him. The point I am trying to make is that <u>ganja</u> <u>does not make one ill</u>. All it does is bring out the reality of whatever state of mind one is in:

- If the mind is carnal, ganja brings it out.

- If the mind is confused ganja brings it out.

- If the mind is feeding on fanasies to do with hurts or grudges from years long past, the ganja brings it out.

- If the mind is drawing upon the fact that one had had a good day at work, the ganja will bring it out.

- If the mind comes to the actual place where one is conceding that there is no hope, the ganja will bring it out.

- If one is pleased about the marks one has scored in one's assignment or exam, then the ganja will help to enhance this deep sense of satisfaction. Ganja is an enhancer. All it does is enhance the state of mind you are in. That's why I would call for a programme of re-education in drugs, so our youths will begin to internalise the purpose of ganja — first of all, 'when to use it, what it is for and guard most of all, against the abuse of its usefulness'.

160

Doreen:

Right now, there are parents out there who can identify with the sorts of problems I myself as a mother have got to go through. Some of their sons come home smoking ganja and can't wake up to go to school next morning. Some see their sons kicked out of college even to the point of losing several jobs. They come in late at night, or early next morning; sleep whole day and if the parent don't tell them to get up, they won't. When they actually get up out of their beds they don't look their 'real' selves. They look more like zombies. The only time they come back to themselves, is when they treat themselves to another spliff to give them a 'high' and you call this life? You call this meditation? When they have lost their 'real' selves, it becomes my problem — not just theirs!

If one needs to open one's mind or find the 'real' self through the paths of meditation, one can do so by cleansing one's self and giving one's thoughts to the Lord. Have a bath, lay in a clean bed and channel one's mind to the Lord...and He will show them whatever they need to know.

In my West Indian upbringing, I was never ever introduced to ganja. Ganja-smoking was socially unacceptable — end of story! Which truthful Jamaican would ignore the usefulness of the 'Jamaica Weekly Gleaner'? It features a whole variety of news. The Gleaner also provides current news about people who are still being arrested for smoking ganja why? Because the law says it's wrong. The smoking of ganja whether in Britain or Jamaica, is still a criminal offence.

My final question is this: What would happen to us dear dear sweet folks if we all decided to smoke ganja? Simple isn't it? THE PRISON POPULATION WOULD BE DOUBLED AND TREBBLED AND QUADRUPLED. Yes? Yes?? No way! This is not what we want for our youths. We want to keep the streets tidy don't we? We want to cut down the level of crime don't we? And the worst part about all this, is the problem of experimenting. Once we have experimented one form of drug, we are likely to take our experiment to a 'harder' form of drug like crack, cocain or heroin. Once we have started with the ganja, the temptation to experiment with harder drugs becomes a real possibility.

OPENING-UP THE WHOLE DEBATE ON GANJA!

Incidentally, I am pleased to invite Jason to share his own viewpoint on the usefulness or better still, misunderstandings that can arise as to ganja and its use. He looks about in his 30s, and by religion, he is a She-vite. In a moment, we will explain the term 'Shevite', but in the mean-time, this is what he has to say about ganja:

"In India the Shevites associate this herb with the sacred attributes of the River Ganges. The Ganges is holy. So is the ganja. Sheva belongs to the pantheon of Hindu gods. Whenever he is portrayed in pictures, he always wear locks, and is intoxicated wth ganja because, it is said to put him on par with the boundless, all-powerful reservoir of peace.

I am a Shevite. All Shevites believe that ganja help them to get in touch with higher and more enlightened states of consciousness. By the way, I am English, and I can remember the first experience that initi-ated me into the peaceful paths of Shevite meditation. This was the first time that I actually smoked ganja. My eyes were opened in such a way that I saw the birds, the bees, the flowers and the rest of Creation in a new light. I felt most of all, a reservoir of love and creative beauty such as I had never ever known before.

By the way, while I was jotting his words on note paper, I had to stop and commend him on how absolutely peaceful he looked. For instance, I asked him if he went to church to worship whenever he was ready to get in touch with the All Powerful Creator. "No", was his reply. He insisted that this was personally an individual path for him and he was happy the way he was. "Many Shevites pursue an individualistic path. First of all, they renounce materialism, much preferring to spend time cultivat-ing tolerance, acceptance and love. Every time he harked back to the first intrinsic experience that drew him to Shevaism, he had to admit that God was real. The goodness of God was real, not only in the works of creation, but within his own heart. He pointed out that the Shevites in a way reminded him of the Rastas since they saw the ganja as a sacred herb emanating from the beauty of a divine Creation.

I then went on to ask him whether or not ganja should be smoked in school.

"With art subjects absolutely yes! Drama, Dance, Music Painting and Drawing. If one is studying Philosophy in a university environment, one's mind opens... One gets closer to one's real self".

162

NEW BORN CHILD: NEW BORN HAPPINESS

I asked him what he meant by 'the real self':

"If you study Literature, Art, Music, Drama or just go to a Creative Dance class, you find you are more in touch with the natural child in you — that natural child that wants to free itself. Every new born child comes with a new born happiness... just the thrill of being able to explore for the first time. Believe me, that newness of experience is heaven-sent and heaven-blessed"!

Gosh! This reminded me so much of the theory of Abraham Maslow. Oh, the way he talks about the 'natural child' in all of us, and the way grown men and women are so frightened to dance, cry, have a good laugh or just relax and be themselves! In a way, this also reminded me of Christ saying to Nicodemus 'except thou becomest a little child, thou canst not enter into the kingdom of heaven'. Today's education system has so bombarded grown men and women with book-learning, and the work place has so inundated us with rules that we eventually turn-out into the frightened people we are.

People unfortunately, are too frightened to cry when they are hurt, or get up and dance when music instils feelings of liberation within the inner soul, or stand with the God-given courage and let their true anger come out. Nobody absolutely nobody should be ashamed of expressing anger!!! One can always apologise afterwards why? Because your anger is your true feelings. Your anger is your real self. I don't believe in any religion that tells you to suppress the real anger you are feeling. Nobody will know what you are feeling unless you express those feelings in language which can be understood! Why hurt inside? Let the hurt come out. If the hurt does not come out then you are likely to be suffering the pains of psychologically injurious repression.

Jason went on to say that one of the reasons world governments put a ban on ganja, is because it awakes people's innate creative powers. The government's idea of conformity and the laws that go with it, are threatened by the liberating powers of ganja. Armies and factory systems help to instil strict control. Hence the rule over the masses inspired by fear to give the masses ultimate control over their lives.

GEORGE IS INVOLVED IN THE NEXT STAGE OF THE GREAT GANJA DEBATE!

"When you smoke ganja it evaporates inside your system. I don't think it is natural to have smoke going through one's body. Although I don't really agree to smoke it, I smoke it none the less. My question is this: 'If this plant is instilling this wonderful insight into the nature of our true selves why not put it into a pot and cook it the same as you would cook vegetable? Why smoke it? Smoke inhalation is not good for anybody's lungs. Tobacco is bad. Ganja can also be bad if not used in moderation. Like any other form of drug, there are guidelines and rules to help determine its appropriate use; if we follow these guidelines, nothing will go wrong.

In today's drug culture, the trouble is people are too frightened to come forward and ask. Rather than displaying their ignorance amongst a certain circle of friends, they would find it easier to 'pretend' they know everything that is to be known about ganja when in fact they don't.

The very first time I smoked ganja — I'll never forget — I felt sick why? Because, I just had a binge of beer-drinking. Now if I had gone up to some trusted friend and asked 'hey pal, when is the best time to smoke ganja', I would have been warned that just about the worst time to smoke ganja, is immediately after one has consumed several pints of beer, then I would have understood you see?

George appears to be piping out Vanessa's message — a message to do with re-educating our youths on how best to employ the use of ganja. If they are using it wrongly, then things unfortunately can go wrong and will go wrong. The same goes for everything else. Incidentally, what I found fascinating about my interview with George, was the way he seemed to analyse the ganja plant. For instance, he made the distinction between the male and female plant. The psychedelic power (otherwise called THC), comes not from the male, but the female plant and it is the bud that produces this wonderful THC. — thank you George for this information!

In my discussion yesterday with a born-again Christian called Lloyd, I found it very very difficult to understand that he was extolling the wonderful virtues of ganja. Lloyd said,

"Ganja is the most sacred gift in the whole of the vegetable kingdom. Ganja is ace", he said. I asked him if he actually smoked it now even though he was a Christian. "Absolutely", he replied.

"There are secrets about ganja", he insisted. "Ganja is a sacred gift from God to man".

Incidentally, I was speaking to another Afro Caribbean male called Gregory: his first name is Jonathan. Boy O boy, this man pipes out some weird new information man! Most of his info gravitates round the beliefs held by the Mission Tabernacle Church of London. Dig this:

"The spiritually correct term for ganja is "poppy". "Poppy" comes from out of the Garden-of-Eden story in the book of Genesis. According to the story, this "poppy" was the fruit of the tree that should not have been touched by Adam and Eve. It stands to reason then, that this is the fruit that brings with it, the knowledge of good and of evil".

Before I go any further, let me bring in Amal ('brother Roger') to hear what he has to say:

"Right, right, this ganja business seems to be taking us all the way up to 'cloud 9'. Frankly, I am suspicious of people who say they see nothing wrong with the stuff, and this is the pure weed coming from out of the natural earth, so much so, terms like 'grand and glorious' are being ascribed to its medicinal value and so forth.

Let me put it this way: the man who is eating his everyday meat will seek to put just as watertight and convincing an argument as the person who is into his vegetarian stuff and all that. In other words, if you are definitely into your ganja, you will seek to defend it to the hilt.

Yes, ganja is medicinal when it comes from out of the soil! Yes, ganja is the essential ingredient that makes its impact in the event of a herbal health-giving bath, but that is when you're in Jamaica. How do you know the ganja we're all talking about is the same thing? For a start, these people call it ash don't they? Let's get this right: the people who 'a get dem liccle weed an ting', are not talking about medicine at all. Medicine is far, far, far from their minds... people are out to have fun... they can't fool me!"

Next please: let me hear what 'Meadows Man' Danny Wilks has got to say 'bout dis ting:

"Greetings, right, hold-up, hold-up! Cigarette — got it? Cigarette (an wen a talkin' to yu pay attention!) is responsible fa more deaths than any other drug — Right? Right!"

This man is right; in fact, he is so right I will have to compare notes with what Dr Mariam Stoppard says in "Drugs Info File" (1999) pages 6 and 10:

"In the U.K. every year, there are around 120,000 smoking related deaths and about 25,000 illegal drug-related deaths so that yes, yes, yes, cigarette is far more harmful than the ganja we're all talking about".

Society heavens man, is so hypocritical! The government must put its house in order by starting the debate not with marijuana, but smoking and drinking, because these two are the killers in our midst right now. Here is an evaluation of the ganja experience coming from yours truly Rob; notice he alternates between ganja and cider:

"I love it, I hate what I have become. Actually, I was into marijuana before...I also got into indoor drinking with cider".

By the way, I stumbled into Rob from out of the A/level Literature from years an' years an' cum again Rob, a fegat wot yu said:

"You see this rr... ganja it makes (it can make) you lazy. Actually, I am very depressed at the mo. Close to having spent £50 of my fortnight's money on this stuff and —".

"I thought money was dead and buried. Any ganja debate without money and its impact is just futile. Say thanks — cheers — Rob for contributing added colour, by opening-up yet another dimension that is needed. People do spend a lot when it comes to drugs; they may even end up spending more than they expected. At the end of the day, people are looking for a way out. My reasons for questioning drugs are manifold. Let us hope we will all be learning something by the end of this debate.

BALANCING BOTH SIDES OF THE GANJA DEBATE

by Spec 'B'

I am pleased the Author has taken it upon himself to accommodate and facilitate such an incredibly wide range of opinions and views around the theme of ganja. I bet you he is actually 'quite surprised' to see how well the debate has taken off, considering it started in essence, between just two persons — <u>Lorraine Mc Hale and Vanessa Graham</u>! Between them both they have actually managed to summon the attention of a Full House with practically everybody wanting to air their views all at the same time — so order! Order in the House please!!.

Incidentally, Mr Browne at last-minute, has quickly drafted me in to see if I can effect a sort of balance between both sides of the debate. I know it won't be easy; having said so, I would none the less like to try:

Yes sir, coming-up: first of all I would like to commend both Vanessa and Lorraine for being so frank and honest in their respective beliefs. If they are anywhere as passionate as they sound on paper, then believe me these women will get things done! Let's check the evidence (s) they have on offer and see how well they stand up. Hence, the question I have for both ladies is this: HAVE ANY OF YOU TRIED THE GANJA WEED TO FIND OUT WHETHER OR NOT IT'S SAFE? To me, the proof of the pudding is in the eating. It is only through personal experience that a man, woman or child can learn. If I am wrong, I' m wrong! Lorraine and Vanessa have not actually let readers know whether they have tried ganja or not, but George has:

> "The very first time I smoked ganja — I'll never forget — I felt sick why? Because I just had a binge of beer drinking. Now if I had gone up to some trusted friend and asked 'hey pal, when is the best time to smoke ganja?'

Hold it right there — do you see what I am getting at? To me, this is real. On the basis of personal experience, this guy can now go on to tell us whether ganja is bad, bad, bad full stop, or good good good. <u>Another good strong source of evidence</u> came from the ganja-smoking youth who literally poured out his heart to Vanessa, thus letting her know some of the heart-breaking experiences which were unsettling him over several months. I can well understand if he said those things had nothing what-

167

soever to do with the smoking of ganja! That one piece of source evidence has helped to give clarity to her full-scale argument. If she is saying well look… 'ganja can be blamed for a lot of things'… I can well believe her! In other words, if there is something to be learned about the advantages and disadvantages of ganja and its use, then let us all learn together and be edified.

Again what I really do appreciate about George, is the fact that he brings out the advantages and disadvantages extremely well:

"When you smoke ganja it evaporates inside your system. I don't think it is natural to have smoke going through one's body… I smoke it nevertheless… My question is this: 'if this plant is instilling this wonderful insight into the nature of our true selves why not put it into a pot and cook it the same as you would cook any other vegetable? Why smoke it? Smoke inhalation is not good for anybody's lungs".

Lorraine is coming from a totally different angle when she brings in the role of parental upbringing especially in regards to which drug is socially acceptable and that which is not:

"In my West Indian upbringing, I was never ever introduced to ganja. Ganja smoking was socially unacceptable full stop".

If she went as far as saying ganja is unacceptable in the eyes of the law, as in the case of being classified a class B drug with a penalty of 5 years imprisonment I would still have to question it? Again, if she is talking about ganja on the Jamaican scene I would hope that this drug is socially acceptable for some. Others may resist its value purely on moral grounds… now I can't quarrel with Jamaican parents for teaching their children ganja-smoking is wrong. I would rather construct more of a question that gives the Government a case to answer…for instance, why are Governments less than honest about the true value of the ganja plant? Why are they conning the people?

Had I not studied this for myself, I would never have known that the Government of the United States legalised the growing of ganja as a 'higly profitable' farming industry i.e. in Virginia (1619), Massachusetts (1631) and Connecticut (1632). And listen to this:

"You could even be jailed in America for not growing cannabis during several periods of shortage".

This excerpt was quoted from "The Emperor Wears No Clothes" by Jack Herer (1993). D'you see what I'm saying? This was 'mandatory by law' — that means you 'must' grow it! <u>As a farmer if you didn't grow it, then you would be in trouble with the law.</u> O.K., O.K., so when did the Government decide to make ganja illegal? In 1937 — yes — <u>in 1937 the same Government of the U.S.A. prohibited not just farmers, but the whole population of America from having anything to do with the growing or smoking of ganja.</u>

Finally, let me respond by drawing something from Jason the Shevite in his treatment of ganja throughout the course of this debate. He has opened-up on the spiritual dimension which is so very fresh and different. This man has stayed not just with the spiritual paths of consciousness, but has chose to highlight some of the benefits derived from ganja especially in relation to studying subjects like Drama, Music, Literature and Philosophy. Again, what Vanessa is calling for is re-education, so students especially in a college environment can access the information that tells when to smoke, and in what quantities...

George has raised an extremely important question for all smokers — be it tobacco or ganja — IS IT HEALTHY TO INHALE SMOKE IN OUR LUNGS? This is the sort of question which cannot honestly be swept underneath any carpet! Another such question comes from Amal (Roger) when he asks:

"HOW DO YOU KNOW THE GANJA WE ARE ALL TALKING ABOUT IS THE SAME AS THE ONE GROWN IN JAMAICA?"

Good gracious! Questions like these for safety sake, must be asked since the possibilities of man-made drug chemicals — like 'skunk' — are real. I suspect he is hinting at the authentic home-grown 'medicinal' ganja to which 'Pegie Man' has made so many references. And speaking of the 'medicinal', I doubt very much if many of the contributors to this debate have said very much about the medicinal properties of the authentic ganja plant. <u>Ganja is good for asthma, glaucoma, nausea, epilepsy, multiple scelrosis, back pains, cystic fibrosis, arthritis, rheumatism and a lot more...</u>I could go on all day all night...by the way Ladies and Gentlemen, I hand you over once again to the Editor himself-

Pitman Browne:

"Nice one Spec 'B'! This was more like a marathon. Thank you for piping-out the views of the people so clearly. One question at the back of my mind throughout the whole of this debate... now... if I was intent on finding-out the usefulness of ganja for myself, would it be OK if I waited till I was ill — then tried a wee bit of 'pure' ganja in drinking form? Well? On that note, I'll say bye-bye to everyone... but just before I go, perhaps I should point out that Doreen McHale was the one who brought the debate to a very serious level of discussion. Vanessa Graham stepped-in at the right time. I feel that members of the public will be seriously challenged by this debate, since both sides are very clearly and meaningfully expressed.

Our youths can't say they haven't learnt anything!